HEINEMANN MODULAR MATHEMATICS
for LONDON AS AND A-LEVEL
Mechanics 4

John Hebborn   Jean Littlewood

Heinemann Educational Publishers,
Halley Court, Jordan Hill, Oxford, OX2 8EJ
a division of Reed Educational & Professional Publishing Ltd

OXFORD FLORENCE PRAGUE MADRID ATHENS
MELBOURNE AUCKLAND KUALA LUMPUR SINGAPORE
TOKYO IBADAN NAIROBI KAMPALA JOHANNESBURG
GABORONE PORTSMOUTH NH (USA) CHICAGO MEXICO CITY
SAO PAULO

First published 1996

99 10 9 8 7 6 5 4 3

ISBN 0435 51806 2

Original design by Geoffrey Wadsley: additional design work by Jim Turner

Typeset and illustrated by Tech-Set Limited, Gateshead, Tyne & Wear

Printed in Great Britain by the Bath Press

Acknowledgements:

The publisher's and authors' thanks are due to the University of London
Examinations and Assessment Council (ULEAC) for permission to reproduce
questions from past examination papers. These are marked with an [L].

The answers have been provided by the authors and are not the responsibility of
the examining board.

About this book

This book is designed to provide you with the best preparation possible for your London Modular Mathematics M4 examination. The series authors are examiners and exam moderators themselves and have a good understanding of the exam board's requirements.

Finding your way around

To help to find your way around when you are studying and revising use the:

- **edge marks** (shown on the front page) – these help you to get to the right chapter quickly;
- **contents list** – this lists the headings that identify key syllabus ideas covered in the book so you can turn straight to them;
- **index** – if you need to find a topic the **bold** number shows where to find the main entry on a topic.

Remembering key ideas

We have provided clear explanations of the key ideas and techniques you need throughout the book. Key ideas you need to remember are listed in a **summary of key points** at the end of each chapter and marked like this in the chapters:

$$\blacksquare \qquad \text{work done} = \int_{x_1}^{x_2} F(x)\mathrm{d}x$$

Exercises and exam questions

In this book questions are carefully graded so they increase in difficulty and gradually bring you up to exam standard.

- **past exam questions** are marked with an L;
- **review exercises** on pages 89 and 157 help you practise answering questions from several areas of mathematics at once, as in the real exam;
- **exam style practice paper** – this is designed to help you prepare for the exam itself;
- **answers** are included at the end of the book – use them to check your work.

Contents

A knowledge and expertise in the contents of Books M1, M2 and M3 and their prerequisites, together with a knowledge of scalar and vector products, differentiation of vectors, polar coordinates, intrinsic coordinates and Maclaurin series is assumed and expected.

Applications of vectors in mechanics

1

1.1 Relative motion

When the motions of two particles A and B relative to a fixed point O are known, then the motion of A relative to B or B relative to A can be studied. An example of such a situation which could be modelled by this is when an observer on one ship A, which is moving, observes the motion of a second ship B, which is also moving. The motion that the observer would see is the motion of B relative to A. Another example would be the problem of 'near misses' of aircraft. It is the motion of one aircraft relative to the other that is of primary importance in avoiding a near miss. Before studying relative motion we will first consider relative positions.

Relative position

Suppose particle A has position vector $\mathbf{r}_A$ relative to a fixed point O and particle B has position vector $\mathbf{r}_B$ relative to the same point. Then a vector triangle can be drawn:

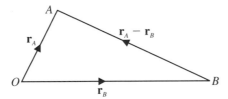

The side BA of the triangle represents the position vector of A relative to B. So

- **position vector of A relative to $B = \mathbf{r}_A - \mathbf{r}_B$**

The position vector of A relative to B is often denoted by ${}_A\mathbf{r}_B$ giving ${}_A\mathbf{r}_B = \mathbf{r}_A - \mathbf{r}_B$.

If the two particles A and B are moving and at some time ${}_A\mathbf{r}_B = \mathbf{0}$ then A and B collide. For two particles which do not collide, the magnitude of the relative position vector is a minimum when the particles are closest together.

Example 1

James and Kevin are kicking a ball to one another. At time $t = 0$, the ball is at the point with position vector $(6\mathbf{i} + 8\mathbf{j})$ m relative to a fixed point O. James then kicks the ball with constant velocity $(\mathbf{i} - 2\mathbf{j})\,\mathrm{m\,s^{-1}}$. At that moment Kevin is at the point with position vector $2\mathbf{i}$ m and he is running with a constant velocity $(3\mathbf{i} + 2\mathbf{j})\,\mathrm{m\,s^{-1}}$. Show that Kevin will intercept the ball and find the position vector of the point of interception.

The position vector $\mathbf{r}_B$ m of the ball at time t seconds is given by:

$$\mathbf{r}_B = 6\mathbf{i} + 8\mathbf{j} + t(\mathbf{i} - 2\mathbf{j})$$

since it starts from the point with position vector $(6\mathbf{i} + 8\mathbf{j})$ m and moves with velocity $(\mathbf{i} - 2\mathbf{j})\,\mathrm{m\,s^{-1}}$.

Kevin's position vector $\mathbf{r}_K$ metres at time t seconds is given by:

$$\mathbf{r}_K = 2\mathbf{i} + t(3\mathbf{i} + 2\mathbf{j})$$

(See the vector equation of a line, Book P3 chapter 6.)

The position vector $_B\mathbf{r}_K$ m of the ball relative to Kevin is therefore given by:

$$_B\mathbf{r}_K = \mathbf{r}_B - \mathbf{r}_K = 6\mathbf{i} + 8\mathbf{j} + t(\mathbf{i} - 2\mathbf{j}) - [2\mathbf{i} + t(3\mathbf{i} + 2\mathbf{j})]$$
$$= (4 - 2t)\mathbf{i} + (8 - 4t)\mathbf{j}$$

Hence $_B\mathbf{r}_K = \mathbf{0}$ when $4 - 2t = 0$ **and** $8 - 4t = 0$.

So $_B\mathbf{r}_K = \mathbf{0}$ when $t = 2$ and Kevin intercepts the ball at that time.

When $t = 2$,

$$\mathbf{r}_K = 2\mathbf{i} + 2(3\mathbf{i} + 2\mathbf{j})$$
$$= 8\mathbf{i} + 4\mathbf{j}$$

So Kevin intercepts the ball at the point with position vector $(8\mathbf{i} + 4\mathbf{j})$ m.

Relative velocity

When two particles A and B are moving we have seen that their position vectors are related by

$$_A\mathbf{r}_B = \mathbf{r}_A - \mathbf{r}_B$$

Differentiating this equation with respect to time gives

$$_A\mathbf{v}_B = \mathbf{v}_A - \mathbf{v}_B$$

where $_A\mathbf{v}_B$ is the velocity of A relative to B and $\mathbf{v}_A$ and $\mathbf{v}_B$ are the velocities of A and B respectively.

This relative velocity equation can be re-written to read

$$\mathbf{v}_A = {}_A\mathbf{v}_B + \mathbf{v}_B$$

or: $$\mathbf{v}_A = \mathbf{v}_B + {}_A\mathbf{v}_B$$

This form of the velocity equation is particularly applicable to problems such as that of a boat being rowed across a river which has a current. The equation shows that the actual velocity of the boat (that is the velocity with which the boat is seen to move) is the resultant of the velocity of the boat relative to the water (that is the speed at which the boat is rowed and the direction in which it is pointed) and the velocity of the water. The actual velocity of an aeroplane experiencing a cross-wind can also be calculated using this equation.

Example 2

A boy who can row at $7\,\mathrm{m\,s}^{-1}$ in still water is rowing across a river in which the current is flowing at $3\,\mathrm{m\,s}^{-1}$.

(a) Determine at what angle to the river bank the boy must steer his boat if he is to reach the point on the far bank directly opposite his starting position

(b) Given that the river is $70\,\mathrm{m}$ wide, calculate the time the boat takes to cross the river.

(a) The speed at which the boy can row in still water gives us the magnitude of the velocity of the boat relative to the water.

Using: $${}_B\mathbf{v}_W + \mathbf{v}_W = \mathbf{v}_B$$

where $\mathbf{v}_B$ is the velocity of the boat and $\mathbf{v}_W$ is the velocity of the water, gives the vector triangle:

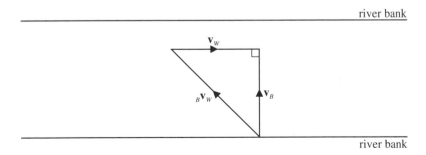

This is a right-angled triangle as the boy is moving across the river to the point directly opposite his starting position.

Using the information given, the diagram becomes:

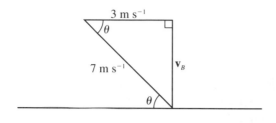

So:
$$\cos \theta = \tfrac{3}{7}$$
$$\theta = 64.6° \quad \text{(to 3 significant figures)}$$

The boy must steer the boat at an angle of 64.6° to the river bank.

(b) To find the time he takes to cross, we must calculate the magnitude of $\mathbf{v}_B$.

By Pythagoras:
$$|\mathbf{v}_B| = \sqrt{(7^2 - 3^2)}\,\mathrm{m\,s}^{-1} = \sqrt{40}\,\mathrm{m\,s}^{-1}$$

The time taken to cross the river is given by:

$$\text{time} = \frac{\text{distance}}{\text{speed}}$$

So: $\text{time} = \tfrac{70}{\sqrt{40}} \text{ seconds} = 11.1 \text{ seconds} \quad \text{(to 3 significant figures)}$

The boy takes 11.1 seconds to cross the river.

Example 3

Gail walks at a speed of $5\,\mathrm{km\,h}^{-1}$ due west and Brian runs at a speed of $12\,\mathrm{km\,h}^{-1}$ in a south easterly direction.

   (a) Find the velocity of Brian relative to Gail.
   (b) Find the speed of Brian relative to Gail and the direction of the relative velocity.

The information given can be summarised by the following diagrams:

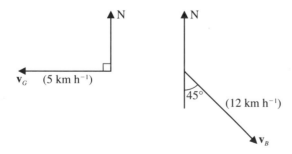

Suppose the unit vector due South is **i** and the unit vector due East is **j**.

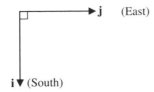

Then the unit vector in the South-East direction is $\frac{1}{\sqrt{2}}(\mathbf{i}+\mathbf{j})$.

So: $\mathbf{v}_G = -5\mathbf{j}\,\text{km h}^{-1}$

And: $\mathbf{v}_B = 12 \times \frac{1}{\sqrt{2}}(\mathbf{i}+\mathbf{j})\,\text{km h}^{-1} = 6\sqrt{2}\,(\mathbf{i}+\mathbf{j})\,\text{km h}^{-1}.$

(a) The velocity of Brian relative to Gail is:

$$_B\mathbf{v}_G = \mathbf{v}_B - \mathbf{v}_G = [6\sqrt{2}\,(\mathbf{i}+\mathbf{j}) + 5\mathbf{j}]\,\text{km h}^{-1}$$
$$= [6\sqrt{2}\mathbf{i} + (6\sqrt{2}+5)\mathbf{j}]\,\text{km h}^{-1}.$$

(b) The speed of Brian relative to Gail is the modulus of this velocity. So:

$$|_B\mathbf{v}_G| = \left[(6\sqrt{2})^2 + (6\sqrt{2}+5)^2\right]^{\frac{1}{2}}\,\text{km h}^{-1}$$
$$= [72 + 72 + 25 + 60\sqrt{2}]^{\frac{1}{2}}\,\text{km h}^{-1}$$
$$= [169 + 60\sqrt{2}]^{\frac{1}{2}}\,\text{km h}^{-1}$$
$$= 15.9\,\text{km h}^{-1}$$

Let the relative velocity make an angle θ with **i**.

Then:

And: $$\tan\theta = \frac{6\sqrt{2}+5}{6\sqrt{2}}$$
$$\theta = 57.8°$$

The speed of Brian relative to Gail is $15.9\,\text{km h}^{-1}$ and the relative velocity is in the direction S $57.8°$ E.

Closest approach

Two particles A and B are closest together when the magnitude of the position vector of A relative to B is a minimum.

That is, when $|_A\mathbf{r}_B| = |_B\mathbf{r}_A|$ is minimum.

Example 4

A and B are two small yachts. At 14.00 hours B has position vector $(3\mathbf{i} + 6\mathbf{j})$ km relative to A. Yacht A has a constant velocity of $(4\mathbf{i} + 6\mathbf{j})$ km h^{-1} and yacht B has a constant velocity of $(5\mathbf{i} - 2\mathbf{j})$ km h^{-1}. By modelling the yachts as particles find, to the nearest minute, the time when A and B are closest together and the distance between them at this time.

Let 14.00 hrs be time $t = 0$.

The velocity of B relative to A, $_B\mathbf{v}_A$ km h^{-1}, is given by:

$$_B\mathbf{v}_A = \mathbf{v}_B - \mathbf{v}_A$$
$$= (5\mathbf{i} - 2\mathbf{j}) - (4\mathbf{i} + 6\mathbf{j})$$
$$= \mathbf{i} - 8\mathbf{j}$$

Then, at time t hrs the position vector of B relative to A, $_B\mathbf{r}_A$ km, is given by:

$$_B\mathbf{r}_A = (3\mathbf{i} + 6\mathbf{j}) + t(\mathbf{i} - 8\mathbf{j})$$
$$= (3 + t)\mathbf{i} + (6 - 8t)\mathbf{j}$$

So: $$|_B\mathbf{r}_A| = \sqrt{[(3 + t)^2 + (6 - 8t)^2]}$$

$|_B\mathbf{r}_A|$ is minimum when $(3 + t)^2 + (6 - 8t)^2$ is minimum.

Let: $$f(t) = (3 + t)^2 + (6 - 8t)^2$$
$$= 9 + 6t + t^2 + 36 - 96t + 64t^2$$
$$= 45 - 90t + 65t^2$$

Differentiating with respect to t gives:

$$\frac{\mathrm{d}}{\mathrm{d}t}f(t) = -90 + 130t$$

For closest approach, $\dfrac{\mathrm{d}}{\mathrm{d}t}f(t) = 0$.

But $\dfrac{\mathrm{d}}{\mathrm{d}t}f(t) = 0$ when $t = \frac{90}{130} = \frac{9}{13}$ hr $= 41.5$ minutes

As $t = 0$ at 14.00 hrs, the yachts are closest together at 14.42 hrs (to the nearest minute).

When $t = \frac{9}{13}$,

$$|_B\mathbf{r}_A| = \sqrt{\left[\left(3 + \tfrac{9}{13}\right)^2 + \left(6 - \tfrac{72}{13}\right)^2\right]}$$
$$= 3.72$$

The distance between the yachts at 14.42 hrs is 3.72 km.

Closest approach using a scalar product

As we have seen, two moving particles A and B are closest together when:

$$|_A\mathbf{r}_B| \text{ is a minimum.}$$

But $|_A\mathbf{r}_B|$ is a minimum when $|_A\mathbf{r}_B|^2$ is a minimum and $|_A\mathbf{r}_B|^2 = {_A\mathbf{r}_B} \cdot {_A\mathbf{r}_B}$. (Book P3 chapter 6)

Differentiating this equation with respect to time gives

$$\frac{\mathrm{d}}{\mathrm{d}t}\left(|_A\mathbf{r}_B|^2\right) = 2\,_A\mathbf{r}_B \cdot {_A\mathbf{v}_B}$$

(by the product rule, Book P2 chapter 8), and since $|_A\mathbf{r}_B|$ is minimum when $\frac{\mathrm{d}}{\mathrm{d}t}\left(|_A\mathbf{r}_B|^2\right) = 0$ this shows that $|_A\mathbf{r}_B|$ is minimum when:

$$_A\mathbf{r}_B \cdot {_A\mathbf{v}_B} = 0$$

This gives us an alternative method of solving closest approach problems which is often more efficient, particularly when $_A\mathbf{r}_B$ and $_A\mathbf{v}_B$ are given in vector form.

Example 5

Use the scalar product method to find the time when the two yachts of example 4 are closest together.

As before: $\qquad\qquad {_B\mathbf{v}_A} = \mathbf{i} - 8\mathbf{j}$

and: $\qquad\qquad\quad {_B\mathbf{r}_A} = (3 + t)\mathbf{i} + (6 - 8t)\mathbf{j}$

So: $\qquad {_B\mathbf{r}_A} \cdot {_B\mathbf{v}_A} = [(3 + t)\mathbf{i} + (6 - 8t)\mathbf{j}] \cdot (\mathbf{i} - 8\mathbf{j})$

$$= (3 + t) - 8(6 - 8t)$$

$$= -45 + 65t$$

$_B\mathbf{r}_A \cdot {_B\mathbf{v}_A} = 0$ when $t = \frac{45}{65} = \frac{9}{13}$ hr $= 41.5$ minutes

Therefore they are closest together at 14.42 hours.

Exercise 1A

1 Relative to a fixed origin O, two particles A and B have position vectors $\mathbf{r}_A$ and $\mathbf{r}_B$ respectively. Find the position vector of A relative to B in the following cases:

(a) $\mathbf{r}_A = (2\mathbf{i} - 5\mathbf{j})\,\mathrm{m}$, $\qquad\qquad \mathbf{r}_B = (6\mathbf{i} + 4\mathbf{j})\,\mathrm{m}$

(b) $\mathbf{r}_A = 6\mathbf{i}\,\mathrm{m}$, $\qquad\qquad\qquad \mathbf{r}_B = (3\mathbf{i} + 7\mathbf{j})\,\mathrm{m}$

(c) $\mathbf{r}_A = (2\mathbf{i} + 4\mathbf{j} - 3\mathbf{k})\,\mathrm{m}$, $\qquad \mathbf{r}_B = (7\mathbf{i} + 4\mathbf{j} - 2\mathbf{k})\,\mathrm{m}$

2 $\mathbf{v}_A$ and $\mathbf{v}_B$ are the velocity vectors of two particles A and B. Find the velocity vector of A relative to B and the speed of A relative to B in the following cases:

(a) $\mathbf{v}_A = (7\mathbf{i} + 2\mathbf{j})\,\mathrm{m\,s}^{-1},$ $\mathbf{v}_B = (2\mathbf{i} - 10\mathbf{j})\,\mathrm{m\,s}^{-1}$

(b) $\mathbf{v}_A = 8\mathbf{i}\,\mathrm{m\,s}^{-1},$ $\mathbf{v}_B = (4\mathbf{i} - 3\mathbf{j})\,\mathrm{m\,s}^{-1}$

(c) $\mathbf{v}_A = (4\mathbf{i} - 2\mathbf{j} + 6\mathbf{k})\,\mathrm{m\,s}^{-1},$ $\mathbf{v}_B = (7\mathbf{i} + 5\mathbf{j} - 3\mathbf{k})\,\mathrm{m\,s}^{-1}$

3 A and B are two aircraft. A has a velocity of $(400\mathbf{i} + 120\mathbf{j})\,\mathrm{m\,s}^{-1}$. The pilot of B sees A to have a velocity of $(200\mathbf{i} - 350\mathbf{j})\,\mathrm{m\,s}^{-1}$. Find the velocity of B in vector form.

4 L and M are two liners. At 15.00 hrs the position vector of the bow of L relative to a fixed origin O is $(3\mathbf{i} + 5\mathbf{j})\,\mathrm{km}$ and the position vector of the stern of M relative to O is $(5\mathbf{i} - 4\mathbf{j})\,\mathrm{km}$. The velocities of L and M are $(6\mathbf{i} - \mathbf{j})\,\mathrm{km\,h}^{-1}$ and $(4\mathbf{i} + 8\mathbf{j})\,\mathrm{km\,h}^{-1}$ respectively. Show that if both liners maintain their velocities a collision will occur. Find the time when they collide and the position vector of the point where they collide.

5 P and Q are two aircraft. At 12 noon, the position vector of the pilot of P relative to a fixed origin O is $(5\mathbf{i} + 7\mathbf{j})\,\mathrm{km}$ and that of the pilot of Q relative to O is $(115\mathbf{i} - 25\mathbf{j})\,\mathrm{km}$. The constant velocity vectors of P and Q are $(100\mathbf{i} - 285\mathbf{j})\,\mathrm{km\,h}^{-1}$ and $(75\mathbf{i} - 135\mathbf{j})\,\mathrm{km\,h}^{-1}$ respectively. Calculate the closest distance between the two pilots and the time to the nearest minute when they are this distance apart.

6 A girl can row a boat at $3\,\mathrm{m\,s}^{-1}$ in still water. She wishes to cross a river in which there is a current of $1.5\,\mathrm{m\,s}^{-1}$ by the shortest route possible. The river is $165\,\mathrm{m}$ wide. Find

(a) the direction in which she must steer the boat and

(b) the time she takes to row across the river.

7 A boy can row his boat at $7\,\mathrm{m\,s}^{-1}$ in still water. He rows with his boat pointing in a direction at an angle of $40°$ to a riverbank in the upstream direction. Given that the river is flowing at $5\,\mathrm{m\,s}^{-1}$ find the speed and direction in which the boy and his boat actually travel.

8 A bird is capable of flying at $80\,\mathrm{km\,h}^{-1}$. It wishes to fly to its nest which is due East of its present position. There is a wind blowing from the northwest at $70\,\mathrm{km\,h}^{-1}$. Find the direction relative to the air in which the bird must fly to reach its nest.

9 Peter is running with speed $7.5\,\text{m s}^{-1}$ in the direction $-3\mathbf{i} + 4\mathbf{j}$ and James is running with speed $6.5\,\text{m s}^{-1}$ in the direction $12\mathbf{i} - 5\mathbf{j}$. At time $t = 0$ Peter passes through the point with position vector $(17\mathbf{i} + 5\mathbf{j})\,\text{m}$ and James passes through the point with position vector $(4\mathbf{i} + 20\mathbf{j})\,\text{m}$ both relative to a fixed origin O.

(a) Find the time in seconds when Peter and James are closest together and the distance they are apart at this time.

(b) When $t = 1\,\text{s}$, James alters his velocity so that he intercepts Peter when $t = 2\,\text{s}$. Find his new velocity in vector form.

10 At time $t = 0$ A and B pass through the points with position vectors $(3\mathbf{i} + 4\mathbf{j} - 2\mathbf{k})\,\text{m}$ and $(2\mathbf{i} - 5\mathbf{j} - \mathbf{k})\,\text{m}$ relative to a fixed origin O. A has velocity $(2\mathbf{i} + 2\mathbf{j} - 5\mathbf{k})\,\text{m s}^{-1}$ and B has velocity $(2.5\mathbf{i} + p\mathbf{j} + q\mathbf{k})\,\text{m s}^{-1}$ where p and q are constants. A and B subsequently collide. Find:

(a) the time when they collide

(b) the values of p and q

(c) the position vector of the point of collision.

1.2 Solution of simple vector differential equations

In chapter 1 of Book M2 and chapter 3 of Book M3, in the study of the motion of a particle moving in a straight line, several differential equations were encountered. The solutions of differential equations of the form $\dfrac{dv}{dt} = \text{f}(v)$, $\dfrac{d^2x}{dt^2} + \omega^2 x = 0$ (simple harmonic motion) and $\dfrac{d^2x}{dt^2} + k\dfrac{dx}{dt} + \omega^2 x = 0$ (damped harmonic motion) were considered.

When a particle is moving in a plane, or in three-dimensional space, the use of vectors can facilitate the study of the motion. The resulting differential equations will then involve vectors.

Motion in a plane when the acceleration is proportional to the velocity

The equation of motion for this type of motion is of the form

$$\frac{d\mathbf{v}}{dt} = k\mathbf{v}$$

This equation appears to be an equation of the 'variables separable' type. However, such an approach suggests the equation:

$$\int \frac{d\mathbf{v}}{\mathbf{v}} = \int dt$$

But the left-hand side of this equation involves both division by a vector and integration with respect to the vector $\mathbf{v}$. Neither of these operations is defined. In order to avoid these problems, start by substituting:

$$\mathbf{v} = u\mathbf{i} + w\mathbf{j}$$

Then:
$$\frac{d\mathbf{v}}{dt} = \frac{du}{dt}\mathbf{i} + \frac{dw}{dt}\mathbf{j}$$

and the equation $\dfrac{d\mathbf{v}}{dt} = k\mathbf{v}$ becomes:

$$\frac{du}{dt}\mathbf{i} + \frac{dw}{dt}\mathbf{j} = k(u\mathbf{i} + w\mathbf{j})$$

Equating coefficients of $\mathbf{i}$ and $\mathbf{j}$ on the two sides of this equation gives:

$$\frac{du}{dt} = ku \qquad \text{and} \qquad \frac{dw}{dt} = kw$$

Each of these equations can be solved by separating the variables:

$$\int \frac{du}{u} = k \int dt \qquad\qquad \int \frac{dw}{w} = k \int dt$$

$$\ln|u| = kt + \ln a \qquad\qquad \ln|w| = kt + \ln b$$

where a is a constant $\qquad\qquad$ where b is a constant

$$\ln\left(\frac{|u|}{a}\right) = kt \qquad\qquad \ln\left(\frac{|w|}{b}\right) = kt$$

$$\frac{u}{a} = e^{kt} \qquad\qquad \frac{w}{b} = e^{kt}$$

$$u = ae^{kt} \qquad\qquad w = be^{kt}$$

Hence:
$$\mathbf{v} = u\mathbf{i} + w\mathbf{j}$$
$$\mathbf{v} = ae^{kt}\mathbf{i} + be^{kt}\mathbf{j}$$
$$\mathbf{v} = e^{kt}(a\mathbf{i} + b\mathbf{j})$$

And so:
$$\mathbf{v} = \mathbf{k}e^{kt}$$

where $\mathbf{k}$ is a constant vector.

Example 6

At time t seconds, the velocity $\mathbf{v}\,\mathrm{m\,s}^{-1}$ of a particle P, moving in a plane, satisfies the differential equation

$$\frac{\mathrm{d}\mathbf{v}}{\mathrm{d}t} = 2\mathbf{v}$$

Given that when $t = 0$, the position vector of P, $\mathbf{r}$ metres, relative to a fixed origin, is $(\mathbf{i} - \mathbf{j})\,\mathrm{m}$ and $\mathbf{v} = (2\mathbf{i} + 3\mathbf{j})$, find an expression for $\mathbf{r}$ in terms of t.

$$\frac{\mathrm{d}\mathbf{v}}{\mathrm{d}t} = 2\mathbf{v}$$

Substituting: $\mathbf{v} = u\mathbf{i} + w\mathbf{j}$

Gives: $\dfrac{\mathrm{d}u}{\mathrm{d}t}\mathbf{i} + \dfrac{\mathrm{d}w}{\mathrm{d}t}\mathbf{j} = 2(u\mathbf{i} + w\mathbf{j})$

And so: $\dfrac{\mathrm{d}u}{\mathrm{d}t} = 2u$ $\qquad\qquad$ $\dfrac{\mathrm{d}w}{\mathrm{d}t} = 2w$

Separating the variables:

$$\int \frac{\mathrm{d}u}{u} = \int 2\,\mathrm{d}t \qquad\qquad \int \frac{\mathrm{d}w}{w} = \int 2\,\mathrm{d}t$$

$$\ln|u| = 2t + a \qquad\qquad \ln|w| = 2t + b$$

When $t = 0$, $\mathbf{v} = 2\mathbf{i} + 3\mathbf{j}$ so $u = 2$ and $w = 3$

Hence: $\ln 2 = a$ and $\ln 3 = b$

So: $\ln|u| = 2t + \ln 2 \qquad\qquad \ln|w| = 2t + \ln 3$

$$\ln\left(\frac{|u|}{2}\right) = 2t \qquad\qquad \ln\left(\frac{|w|}{3}\right) = 2t$$

$$u = 2\mathrm{e}^{2t} \qquad\qquad w = 3\mathrm{e}^{2t}$$

So: $\mathbf{v} = 2\mathrm{e}^{2t}\mathbf{i} + 3\mathrm{e}^{2t}\mathbf{j}$

And: $\dfrac{\mathrm{d}\mathbf{r}}{\mathrm{d}t} = 2\mathrm{e}^{2t}\mathbf{i} + 3\mathrm{e}^{2t}\mathbf{j}$

This first order differential equation poses no problems as the solution involves integration with respect to the *scalar* quantity t and $\mathbf{i}$ and $\mathbf{j}$ are constant vectors.

Integrating with respect to t gives:

$$\mathbf{r} = \int \left(2\mathrm{e}^{2t}\,\mathbf{i} + 3\mathrm{e}^{2t}\mathbf{j}\right)\mathrm{d}t$$

$$\mathbf{r} = \mathrm{e}^{2t}\mathbf{i} + \tfrac{3}{2}\mathrm{e}^{2t}\mathbf{j} + c\mathbf{i} + d\mathbf{j}$$

where c and d are constants.

As $\mathbf{r} = \mathbf{i} - \mathbf{j}$ when $t = 0$

$$\mathbf{i} - \mathbf{j} = \mathbf{i} + \tfrac{3}{2}\mathbf{j} + c\mathbf{i} + d\mathbf{j}$$

Equating coefficients of $\mathbf{i}$ on the two sides of this equation gives:

$$1 = 1 + c$$

So:
$$c = 0$$

Equating coefficients of $\mathbf{j}$ on the two sides of this equation gives:

$$-1 = \tfrac{3}{2} + d$$

So:
$$d = -\tfrac{5}{2}$$

Therefore:
$$\mathbf{r} = e^{2t}\mathbf{i} + \left(\tfrac{3}{2}e^{2t} - \tfrac{5}{2}\right)\mathbf{j}$$

Motion in three-dimensional space when the acceleration is proportional to the velocity

The equation of motion for this type of motion is the same as when the movement is restricted to a plane. That is, the equation of motion is:

$$\frac{d\mathbf{v}}{dt} = k\mathbf{v}$$

However, as we are now dealing with three-dimensional vectors, the required substitution is:

$$\mathbf{v} = u\mathbf{i} + w\mathbf{j} + s\mathbf{k}$$

Comparing the three-dimensional and two-dimensional substitutions and considering the two-dimensional solution shows that the three-dimensional solution now becomes:

$$\mathbf{v} = e^{kt}(a\mathbf{i} + b\mathbf{j} + c\mathbf{k})$$

or
$$\mathbf{v} = \mathbf{K}e^{kt}$$

where $\mathbf{K}$ is a constant three-dimensional vector.

Solution of the vector form of the equation for damped harmonic motion

In order to solve the equation

$$\frac{d^2\mathbf{r}}{dt^2} + 2k\frac{d\mathbf{r}}{dt} + (k^2 + n^2)\mathbf{r} = \mathbf{0}$$

substitute $\mathbf{r} = x\mathbf{i} + y\mathbf{j}$ to obtain scalar equations as before.

The equation then becomes:

$$\left(\frac{d^2x}{dt^2}\mathbf{i} + \frac{d^2y}{dt^2}\mathbf{j}\right) + 2k\left(\frac{dx}{dt}\mathbf{i} + \frac{dy}{dt}\mathbf{j}\right) + (k^2 + n^2)(x\mathbf{i} + y\mathbf{j}) = \mathbf{0}.$$

This gives the two scalar equations

$$\frac{d^2x}{dt^2} + 2k\frac{dx}{dt} + (k^2 + n^2)x = 0 \qquad (1)$$

and:

$$\frac{d^2y}{dt^2} + 2k\frac{dy}{dt} + (k^2 + n^2)y = 0 \qquad (2)$$

These equations can be solved using the methods discussed in Book P3 chapter 8:

The auxiliary equation for equation (1) is

$$\lambda^2 + 2k\lambda + (k^2 + n^2) = 0$$

(The auxiliary equation for equation (2) is the same.)

This may be written as:

$$(\lambda + k)^2 + n^2 = 0$$

or: $$(\lambda + k)^2 = -n^2$$

So: $$\lambda + k = \pm ni$$

And: $$\lambda = -k \pm ni$$

(You can also obtain this result by using the quadratic formula to solve the equation.)

Hence the general solutions of equations (1) and (2) are:

$$x = e^{-kt}(A\cos nt + B\sin nt)$$

and: $$y = e^{-kt}(\alpha\cos nt + \beta\sin nt)$$

where A, B, α and β are constants.

And so: $\quad \mathbf{r} = e^{-kt}[(A\cos nt + B\sin nt)\mathbf{i} + (\alpha\cos nt + \beta\sin nt)\mathbf{j}]$

or: $\quad \mathbf{r} = e^{-kt}[(A\mathbf{i} + \alpha\mathbf{j})\cos nt + (B\mathbf{i} + \beta\mathbf{j})\sin nt]$

Writing: $\quad \mathbf{a} = A\mathbf{i} + \alpha\mathbf{j}$

and: $\quad \mathbf{b} = B\mathbf{i} + \beta\mathbf{j}$

gives: $\quad \mathbf{r} = e^{-kt}(\mathbf{a}\cos nt + \mathbf{b}\sin nt)$

where $\mathbf{a}$ and $\mathbf{b}$ are constant vectors.

Notice that this has the same form as the general solution of the differential equation

$$\frac{d^2 z}{dt^2} + 2k\frac{dz}{dt} + (k^2 + n^2)z = 0$$

with the arbitrary scalar constants being replaced by arbitrary constant vectors.

The above solution was obtained assuming that the motion took place in a plane as the substitution used was $\mathbf{r} = x\mathbf{i} + y\mathbf{j}$. The arbitrary constant vectors in the solution in this case are two-dimensional. For three-dimensional motion the substitution required is $\mathbf{r} = x\mathbf{i} + y\mathbf{j} + z\mathbf{k}$ and the arbitrary constant vectors in the resulting solution will be three-dimensional.

Example 7

The position vector $\mathbf{r}$ metres, relative to a fixed origin O, of the particle P at time t seconds is such that $\mathbf{r}$ satisfies the differential equation:

$$\frac{d^2\mathbf{r}}{dt^2} - 2\frac{d\mathbf{r}}{dt} + 5\mathbf{r} = \mathbf{0}$$

Given that when $t = 0$, $\mathbf{r} = 2\mathbf{i} - \mathbf{j}$ and $\dfrac{d\mathbf{r}}{dt} = \mathbf{i} + \mathbf{j}$ find:

(a) an expression for $\mathbf{r}$ in terms of t

(b) the distance of the particle from O when $t = 1$.

(a) $$\frac{d^2\mathbf{r}}{dt^2} - 2\frac{d\mathbf{r}}{dt} + 5\mathbf{r} = \mathbf{0}$$

The auxiliary equation is: $\lambda^2 - 2\lambda + 5 = 0$

$$(\lambda - 1)^2 - 1 + 5 = 0$$

$$(\lambda - 1)^2 = -4$$

$$\lambda = 1 \pm 2i$$

Hence the general solution is:

$$\mathbf{r} = e^t(\mathbf{a}\cos 2t + \mathbf{b}\sin 2t) \tag{1}$$

Since: $\mathbf{r} = 2\mathbf{i} - \mathbf{j}$ when $t = 0$:

$$2\mathbf{i} - \mathbf{j} = \mathbf{a} \tag{2}$$

as $e^0 = 1$, $\cos 0 = 1$ and $\sin 0 = 0$

Differentiating equation (1) with respect to t gives (by the product rule):

$$\frac{d\mathbf{r}}{dt} = e^t(\mathbf{a}\cos 2t + \mathbf{b}\sin 2t) + e^t(-2\mathbf{a}\sin 2t + 2\mathbf{b}\cos 2t)$$

Since $\dfrac{d\mathbf{r}}{dt} = \mathbf{i} + \mathbf{j}$ when $t = 0$,

$$\mathbf{i} + \mathbf{j} = \mathbf{a} + 2\mathbf{b}$$

From equation (2) $\mathbf{a} = 2\mathbf{i} - \mathbf{j}$, so:

$$\mathbf{i} + \mathbf{j} = 2\mathbf{i} - \mathbf{j} + 2\mathbf{b}$$
$$2\mathbf{b} = -\mathbf{i} + 2\mathbf{j}$$

So:
$$\mathbf{b} = -\tfrac{1}{2}\mathbf{i} + \mathbf{j}$$

And:
$$\mathbf{r} = e^{t}\left[(2\mathbf{i} - \mathbf{j})\cos 2t + \left(-\tfrac{1}{2}\mathbf{i} + \mathbf{j}\right)\sin 2t\right]$$

(b) When $t = 1$, $\mathbf{r} = e\left[(2\mathbf{i} - \mathbf{j})\cos 2 + \left(-\tfrac{1}{2} + \mathbf{j}\right)\sin 2\right]$

$$= e\left[\left(2\cos 2 - \tfrac{1}{2}\sin 2\right)\mathbf{i} + (\sin 2 - \cos 2)\mathbf{j}\right]$$

The distance of the particle from O is $|\mathbf{r}|$ where:

$$|\mathbf{r}| = e\sqrt{\left[\left(2\cos 2 - \tfrac{1}{2}\sin 2\right)^{2} + (\sin 2 - \cos 2)^{2}\right]}$$

Remember that radians must be used for this calculation.

So:
$$|\mathbf{r}| = 5.02$$

The distance of the particle from O when $t = 1$ is $5.02\,\text{m}$.

The solution of the vector equation $\dfrac{d\mathbf{r}}{dt} + f(t)\mathbf{r} = \mathbf{a}e^{bt}$ where a and b are constants

The solution of an equation of this type requires the use of an integrating factor (see Book P3 chapter 8).

The integrating factor needed here is $e^{\int f(t)dt}$.

Multiplying the differential equation on both sides by the integrating factor gives:

$$e^{\int f(t)dt}\frac{d\mathbf{r}}{dt} + e^{\int f(t)dt}\cdot f(t)\cdot\mathbf{r} = \mathbf{a}e^{\int f(t)dt}\cdot e^{bt}$$

And so:
$$\frac{d}{dt}\left(e^{\int f(t)dt}\cdot\mathbf{r}\right) = \mathbf{a}e^{\left(\int f(t)dt + bt\right)}$$

Hence integrating with respect to time gives:

$$\mathbf{r}\cdot e^{\int f(t)dt} = \mathbf{a}\int e^{\left(\int f(t)dt + bt\right)}dt$$

and therefore a solution can be obtained for $\mathbf{r}$.

Example 8

At time t seconds the position vector of a particle P relative to a fixed origin is $\mathbf{r}$ metres and satisfies the differential equation:

$$\frac{d\mathbf{r}}{dt} + 5\mathbf{r} = (3\mathbf{i} + 2\mathbf{j} + \mathbf{k})e^t$$

Given that P is at O when $t = 0$, find an expression for $\mathbf{r}$ in terms of t.

$$\frac{d\mathbf{r}}{dt} + 5\mathbf{r} = (3\mathbf{i} + 2\mathbf{j} + \mathbf{k})e^t$$

The integrating factor required is:

$$e^{\int 5dt} = e^{5t}$$

Multiplying the equation by the integrating factor gives:

$$e^{5t}\frac{d\mathbf{r}}{dt} + 5\mathbf{r}e^{5t} = (3\mathbf{i} + 2\mathbf{j} + \mathbf{k})e^t \cdot e^{5t}$$

$$\frac{d}{dt}\left(\mathbf{r}e^{5t}\right) = (3\mathbf{i} + 2\mathbf{j} + \mathbf{k})e^{6t}$$

Integrating with respect to t gives:

$$\mathbf{r}e^{5t} = (3\mathbf{i} + 2\mathbf{j} + \mathbf{k}) \cdot \tfrac{1}{6}e^{6t} + \mathbf{c}$$

where $\mathbf{c}$ is a constant vector.

When $t = 0$, $\mathbf{r} = \mathbf{0}$ so:

$$\mathbf{0} = \tfrac{1}{6}(3\mathbf{i} + 2\mathbf{j} + \mathbf{k}) + \mathbf{c}$$

$$\mathbf{c} = -\tfrac{1}{6}(3\mathbf{i} + 2\mathbf{j} + \mathbf{k})$$

And so: $\quad \mathbf{r}e^{5t} = \tfrac{1}{6}(3\mathbf{i} + 2\mathbf{j} + \mathbf{k})e^{6t} - \tfrac{1}{6}(3\mathbf{i} + 2\mathbf{j} + \mathbf{k})$

Dividing by e^{5t} to obtain an expression for $\mathbf{r}$ gives:

$$\mathbf{r} = \tfrac{1}{6}(3\mathbf{i} + 2\mathbf{j} + \mathbf{k})\left(e^t - e^{-5t}\right)$$

Exercise 1B

1 At time t seconds, the position vector of a particle P, relative to a fixed origin O, is $\mathbf{r}$ metres and its velocity is $\mathbf{v}\,\mathrm{m\,s}^{-1}$. The particle moves so that $\mathbf{v}$ satisfies the differential equation

$$\frac{d\mathbf{v}}{dt} = 4\mathbf{v}.$$

Given that $\mathbf{r} = 4\mathbf{i}$ and $\mathbf{v} = 2\mathbf{i} - 3\mathbf{j}$ when $t = 0$, find $\mathbf{r}$ in terms of t.

2 A particle moves so that its velocity $\mathbf{v}\,\mathrm{m\,s}^{-1}$ at time t seconds satisfies the differential equation $\dfrac{\mathrm{d}\mathbf{v}}{\mathrm{d}t} + 4\mathbf{v} = \mathbf{0}$. The position vector of the particle at time t seconds is $\mathbf{r}$ metres relative to a fixed origin O. Given that $\mathbf{r} = 3\mathbf{i} - 3\mathbf{j}$ and $\mathbf{v} = 2\mathbf{i}$ when $t = 0$ find:

(a) $\mathbf{r}$ in terms of t

(b) the distance of the particle from O when $t = 2$.

3 A particle moves so that its velocity $\mathbf{v}\,\mathrm{m\,s}^{-1}$ at time t seconds satisfies the differential equation $\dfrac{\mathrm{d}\mathbf{v}}{\mathrm{d}t} = 2\mathbf{v}$. Given that $\mathbf{v} = 4\mathbf{i} + 2\mathbf{j}$ when $t = 0$ find:

(a) $\mathbf{v}$ in terms of t

(b) the speed of the particle when $t = 4$.

4 The position vector $\mathbf{r}$ metres of a particle, relative to a fixed origin O, at time t seconds satisfies the differential equation:

$$\frac{\mathrm{d}^2\mathbf{r}}{\mathrm{d}t^2} + 2\frac{\mathrm{d}\mathbf{r}}{\mathrm{d}t} + 5\mathbf{r} = \mathbf{0}.$$

Given that when $t = 0$, $\mathbf{r} = \mathbf{i} + \mathbf{j}$ and $\dfrac{\mathrm{d}\mathbf{r}}{\mathrm{d}t} = \mathbf{i}$, find $\mathbf{r}$ in terms of t and the distance of the particle from O when $t = \dfrac{\pi}{4}$.

5 The position vector $\mathbf{r}$ metres, relative to a fixed origin O, of a particle at time t seconds satisfies the differential equation:

$$\frac{\mathrm{d}^2\mathbf{r}}{\mathrm{d}t^2} + 16\mathbf{r} = \mathbf{0}.$$

Given that $\mathbf{r} = 2\mathbf{i} + 2\mathbf{j}$ and $\dfrac{\mathrm{d}\mathbf{r}}{\mathrm{d}t} = 4\mathbf{i} - 8\mathbf{j}$ when $t = 0$, find $\mathbf{r}$ in terms of t.

6 The position vector $\mathbf{r}$ metres, relative to a fixed origin O, of a particle at time t seconds satisfies the differential equation:

$$\frac{\mathrm{d}^2\mathbf{r}}{\mathrm{d}t^2} + 2\frac{\mathrm{d}\mathbf{r}}{\mathrm{d}t} + \mathbf{r} = \mathbf{0}.$$

Given that when $t = 0$, $\mathbf{r} = \mathbf{i} + 2\mathbf{j}$ and $\dfrac{\mathrm{d}\mathbf{r}}{\mathrm{d}t} = \mathbf{i} - \mathbf{j}$, find $\mathbf{r}$ in terms of t.

7 The position vector **r** metres, relative to a fixed origin O, of a particle P at time t seconds satisfies the differential equation:

$$\frac{d\mathbf{r}}{dt} + 2\mathbf{r} = (15\mathbf{i} + 10\mathbf{j})e^{3t}.$$

When $t = 0$, P is at the point with position vector $2\mathbf{i} + \mathbf{j}$. Find **r** in terms of t.

8 At time t seconds, the position vector of a particle P of mass 1 kg, relative to a fixed origin O, is **r** metres and its velocity is **v** m s^{-1}. The equation of motion for P is $\dfrac{d\mathbf{v}}{dt} = 2\mathbf{v}$.

Given that $\mathbf{r} = 2\mathbf{i} + 4\mathbf{k}$ and $\mathbf{v} = \mathbf{i} + \mathbf{j} + \mathbf{k}$ when $t = 0$, find **r** in terms of t. Calculate the speed of P when $t = 2$.

9 The position vector **r** metres, relative to a fixed origin O, of a particle P at time t seconds satisfies the differential equation:

$$\frac{d^2\mathbf{r}}{dt^2} + 4\frac{d\mathbf{r}}{dt} + 5\mathbf{r} = \mathbf{0}.$$

Given that when $t = 0$, $\mathbf{r} = \mathbf{i} + 2\mathbf{j} + \mathbf{k}$ and $\dfrac{d\mathbf{r}}{dt} = \mathbf{k}$, find:

(a) **r** in terms of t

(b) the distance of the particle from O when $t = \dfrac{\pi}{2}$.

10 The position vector **r** metres, relative to a fixed origin O, of a particle P at time t seconds satisfies the differential equation:

$$\frac{d\mathbf{r}}{dt} + \mathbf{r} = \mathbf{k}e^{t}$$

When $t = 0$, $r = 2\mathbf{i} + 3\mathbf{j} + \mathbf{k}$. Find **r** in terms of t.

1.3 Work done by a constant force

Consider a particle P which is being moved along a horizontal plane by a horizontal force **F** which is acting at an angle θ to the direction of motion of the particle.

The work done by the force **F** as P moves a distance d along the plane is the scalar quantity given by $F \cos \theta \times d$ where F is the magnitude of **F**.

Let the vector **d** be the displacement of P during this time. That is, d is the magnitude of **d**.

Then: work done $= F \cos \theta \times d$ is equivalent to

- **work done $=$ F.d**   (Book P3 chapter 6)

Example 9

A particle P is acted upon by a total force **F** where $\mathbf{F} = (5\mathbf{i} - 2\mathbf{j} + 3\mathbf{k})\,\text{N}$. Calculate the work done by **F** as P moves from the point A with position vector $\mathbf{r}_A = (6\mathbf{i} + 5\mathbf{j} + \mathbf{k})$ metres relative to the origin, O, to the point B with position vector $\mathbf{r}_B = (8\mathbf{i} - 7\mathbf{j} + 6\mathbf{k})$ metres relative to O.

The displacement vector of P is $\overrightarrow{AB}$.

$$\overrightarrow{AB} = \mathbf{r}_B - \mathbf{r}_A = (8\mathbf{i} - 7\mathbf{j} + 6\mathbf{k}) - (6\mathbf{i} + 5\mathbf{j} + \mathbf{k})$$
$$= 2\mathbf{i} - 12\mathbf{j} + 5\mathbf{k}$$

Work done $=$ **F.d**
$$= (5\mathbf{i} - 2\mathbf{j} + 3\mathbf{k}) \,.\, (2\mathbf{i} - 12\mathbf{j} + 5\mathbf{k})$$
$$= 10 + 24 + 15$$
$$= 49$$

The work done by **F** as P moves from A to B is $49\,\text{J}$.

Example 10

A small smooth ring of mass $0.5\,\text{kg}$ moves along a smooth, straight wire. The only forces acting on the ring are a constant force $\mathbf{F} = (5\mathbf{i} + 2\mathbf{j} - 3\mathbf{k})\,\text{N}$ and the normal contact force due to the wire. The ring is initially at rest at the point P with position vector $(\mathbf{i} + \mathbf{j} + \mathbf{k})\,\text{m}$. Find the speed of the ring, in m s^{-1}, as it passes through the point Q with position vector $(3\mathbf{i} + 2\mathbf{j} - \mathbf{k})\,\text{m}$.

The displacement vector of the ring is

$$\mathbf{d} = \mathbf{r}_Q - \mathbf{r}_P$$
$$= (3\mathbf{i} + 2\mathbf{j} - \mathbf{k}) - (\mathbf{i} + \mathbf{j} + \mathbf{k})$$
$$= 2\mathbf{i} + \mathbf{j} - 2\mathbf{k}$$

Work done $=$ **F.d**
$$= (5\mathbf{i} + 2\mathbf{j} - 3\mathbf{k}) \,.\, (2\mathbf{i} + \mathbf{j} - 2\mathbf{k})$$
$$= 10 + 2 + 6$$
$$= 18$$

The work done by **F** is $18\,\text{J}$.

The normal contact force is at right angles to the direction of motion and therefore does no work.

By the work-energy principle, the gain in kinetic energy of the ring is therefore 18 J.

Initial K.E. of ring $= 0$

Final K.E. of ring $= \frac{1}{2}mv^2 = \frac{1}{2} \times 0.5v^2 = \frac{1}{4}v^2$

So:
$$\frac{1}{4}v^2 = 18$$
$$v^2 = 72$$
$$v = 8.485$$

The speed of the ring as it passes through Q is $8.49 \, \text{m s}^{-1}$.

1.4 The vector moment of a force

Consider a force $\mathbf{F}$ and let P be any point on the line of action of $\mathbf{F}$ with position vector $\mathbf{r}$ relative to the origin O. Let the angle between $\mathbf{r}$ and the line of action of $\mathbf{F}$ be θ.

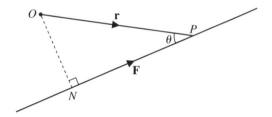

The moment of the force $\mathbf{F}$ about O has been defined in Book M1 chapter 6 to be:

$$ON \times F = r \sin \theta \times F$$

where r and F are the magnitudes of $\mathbf{r}$ and $\mathbf{F}$ respectively.

But the magnitude of $\mathbf{r} \times \mathbf{F}$ is also $r \sin \theta \times F$. This suggests the following definition:

■ **The vector moment of the force $\mathbf{F}$ about the origin O is given by:**

$$\text{vector moment of force} = \mathbf{r} \times \mathbf{F}$$

where $\mathbf{r}$ is the position vector, relative to O, of any point on the line of action of $\mathbf{F}$.

Note that the moment of a force is a vector, that is, it has both magnitude and direction. It is directed along the perpendicular through O to the plane containing $\mathbf{r}$ and $\mathbf{F}$. From the definition of the vector product the direction of $\mathbf{r} \times \mathbf{F}$ along this perpendicular is in the sense of a right-handed screw, turned from $\mathbf{r}$ to $\mathbf{F}$. This gives:

Example 11

The force $\mathbf{F}$ where $\mathbf{F} = (5\mathbf{i} - 2\mathbf{j} + 3\mathbf{k})\,\text{N}$ acts through the point P whose position vector, relative to the origin O, is given by $\mathbf{r}_P = (2\mathbf{i} + 3\mathbf{j} + 4\mathbf{k})\,\text{m}$.

Find the magnitude of the moment of $\mathbf{F}$

    (a) about O
    (b) about the point A with position vector $\mathbf{r}_A = (3\mathbf{i} + 2\mathbf{j})$.

(a)   Vector moment about $O = \mathbf{r}_P \times \mathbf{F}$

$$= (2\mathbf{i} + 3\mathbf{j} + 4\mathbf{k}) \times (5\mathbf{i} - 2\mathbf{j} + 3\mathbf{k})$$

$$= \begin{vmatrix} \mathbf{i} & \mathbf{j} & \mathbf{k} \\ 2 & 3 & 4 \\ 5 & -2 & 3 \end{vmatrix}$$

$$= 17\mathbf{i} + 14\mathbf{j} - 19\mathbf{k}$$

The magnitude of the vector moment $= |17\mathbf{i} + 14\mathbf{j} - 19\mathbf{k}|$

$$= \sqrt{(17^2 + 14^2 + 19^2)}$$

$$= 29.1$$

The magnitude of the vector moment of $\mathbf{F}$ about O is 29.1 Nm.

(b) To find the vector moment of $\mathbf{F}$ about A, we first find the vector $\overrightarrow{AP}$.

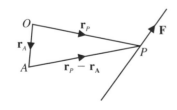

$$\overrightarrow{AP} = \mathbf{r}_P - \mathbf{r}_A$$

$$= (2\mathbf{i} + 3\mathbf{j} + 4\mathbf{k}) - (3\mathbf{i} + 2\mathbf{j})$$

$$= -\mathbf{i} + \mathbf{j} + 4\mathbf{k}$$

Vector moment of $\mathbf{F}$ about $A = \overrightarrow{AP} \times \mathbf{F}$

$$= (-\mathbf{i} + \mathbf{j} + 4\mathbf{k}) \times (5\mathbf{i} - 2\mathbf{j} + 3\mathbf{k})$$

$$= \begin{vmatrix} \mathbf{i} & \mathbf{j} & \mathbf{k} \\ -1 & 1 & 4 \\ 5 & -2 & 3 \end{vmatrix}$$

$$= 11\mathbf{i} + 23\mathbf{j} - 3\mathbf{k}$$

The magnitude of the vector moment $= \sqrt{(11^2 + 23^2 + 3^2)}$

$$= 25.7$$

The magnitude of the vector moment of $\mathbf{F}$ about A is 25.7 Nm.

Exercise 1C

1 In each of the following problems, calculate the work done by the force $\mathbf{F}$ as it moves a particle through the displacement $\mathbf{r}$.
   (a) $\mathbf{F} = (5\mathbf{i} + 7\mathbf{j} + 9\mathbf{k})\,\mathrm{N}$, $\mathbf{r} = (-\mathbf{i} + 5\mathbf{j} - 2\mathbf{k})\,\mathrm{m}$.
   (b) $\mathbf{F} = (9\mathbf{i} - 2\mathbf{j} - 5\mathbf{k})\,\mathrm{N}$, $\mathbf{r} = (2\mathbf{i} + 7\mathbf{j} - 3\mathbf{k})\,\mathrm{m}$.
   (c) $\mathbf{F} = (-2\mathbf{i} + 7\mathbf{j} - 3\mathbf{k})\,\mathrm{N}$, $\mathbf{r} = (4\mathbf{i} + 2\mathbf{j} + \mathbf{k})\,\mathrm{m}$.

2 In each of the following problems, calculate the work done by the force $\mathbf{F}$ as it moves a particle P from the point A with position vector $\mathbf{r}_A$, relative to the origin, O, to the point B with position vector $\mathbf{r}_B$ relative to O.
   (a) $\mathbf{F} = (3\mathbf{i} + 2\mathbf{j} + \mathbf{k})\,\mathrm{N}$, $\mathbf{r}_A = (6\mathbf{i} - 2\mathbf{j} + \mathbf{k})\,\mathrm{m}$, $\mathbf{r}_B = (7\mathbf{i} + 6\mathbf{j} + 5\mathbf{k})\,\mathrm{m}$.
   (b) $\mathbf{F} = (4\mathbf{i} - \mathbf{j} - 2\mathbf{k})\,\mathrm{N}$, $\mathbf{r}_A = (\mathbf{i} + 2\mathbf{j} + 3\mathbf{k})\,\mathrm{m}$, $\mathbf{r}_B = (10\mathbf{i} + 8\mathbf{j} + 6\mathbf{k})\,\mathrm{m}$.
   (c) $\mathbf{F} = (-2\mathbf{i} + 7\mathbf{j} - \mathbf{k})\,\mathrm{N}$, $\mathbf{r}_A = (3\mathbf{i} + 2\mathbf{j} + 3\mathbf{k})\,\mathrm{m}$, $\mathbf{r}_B = (\mathbf{i} + 2\mathbf{j} - \mathbf{k})\,\mathrm{m}$.

3 Given that the particle P in question 2 has mass 2.5 kg and that P starts from rest at point A, calculate in each case the speed of P as it passes through the point B. You may assume that the force $\mathbf{F}$ is the only force doing work on P during the motion.

4 A particle P is acted upon by three forces of magnitude 5 N, 4 N and 10 N acting in the directions of the vectors $2\mathbf{i} + \mathbf{j} + 2\mathbf{k}$, $6\mathbf{i} + 8\mathbf{j}$ and $\mathbf{i} + 8\mathbf{j} + 4\mathbf{k}$ respectively. The three forces cause a displacement of $(7\mathbf{i} - 2\mathbf{j})\,\mathrm{m}$. Find
   (a) the resultant of the three forces
   (b) the total work done by the three forces.

5 In each of the following problems find the vector moment about O of the force $\mathbf{F}$ which passes through the point with position vector $\mathbf{r}$ relative to O.

(a) $\mathbf{F} = (5\mathbf{i} + 6\mathbf{j} + 7\mathbf{k})\,\mathrm{N}, \qquad \mathbf{r} = (2\mathbf{i} - 2\mathbf{j} + 2\mathbf{k})\,\mathrm{m}.$

(b) $\mathbf{F} = (-9\mathbf{i} + 2\mathbf{j} + 5\mathbf{k})\,\mathrm{N}, \qquad \mathbf{r} = (3\mathbf{i} + 7\mathbf{j} - 2\mathbf{k})\,\mathrm{m}.$

(c) $\mathbf{F} = (2\mathbf{i} - 7\mathbf{j} - 4\mathbf{k})\,\mathrm{N}, \qquad \mathbf{r} = (4\mathbf{i} - 2\mathbf{j} - 3\mathbf{k})\,\mathrm{m}.$

6 In each of the following problems, find the vector moment about the point P of the force $\mathbf{F}$ which passes through the point with position vector $\mathbf{r}$ relative to the origin O.

(a) $\mathbf{F} = (5\mathbf{i} + 6\mathbf{j} + 7\mathbf{k})\,\mathrm{N}, \quad \mathbf{r} = (2\mathbf{i} - 2\mathbf{j} + 2\mathbf{k})\,\mathrm{m} \qquad P \text{ is } (2, 3, 4)$

(b) $\mathbf{F} = (4\mathbf{i} - 2\mathbf{j} + 3\mathbf{k})\,\mathrm{N}, \quad \mathbf{r} = (3\mathbf{i} - 7\mathbf{j} + 3\mathbf{k})\,\mathrm{m} \qquad P \text{ is } (1, 0, -1)$

(c) $\mathbf{F} = (3\mathbf{i} - 3\mathbf{j} + 2\mathbf{k})\,\mathrm{N}, \quad \mathbf{r} = (4\mathbf{i} - 4\mathbf{j} - 2\mathbf{k})\,\mathrm{m} \qquad P \text{ is } (1, -2, 3)$

7 The line of action of a force $\mathbf{F}$ of magnitude 15 N is parallel to the vector $3\mathbf{i} + 4\mathbf{k}$ and passes through the point with position vector $(3\mathbf{i} + 3\mathbf{j} - 4\mathbf{k})\,\mathrm{m}$ relative to the origin O. Find the vector moment of $\mathbf{F}$

(a) about the origin

(b) about the point with position vector $(5\mathbf{i} + 3\mathbf{j} + \mathbf{k})\,\mathrm{m}$ relative to O.

8 The force $\mathbf{F}$ is given by $\mathbf{F} = (2\mathbf{i} + 3\mathbf{j} + 2\mathbf{k})\,\mathrm{N}$. The vector moment of $\mathbf{F}$ about the origin is $(5\mathbf{i} - 14\mathbf{j} + 16\mathbf{k})\,\mathrm{Nm}$. A point A on the line of action of $\mathbf{F}$ has position vector $(x\mathbf{i} + y\mathbf{j} + z\mathbf{k})\,\mathrm{m}$ relative to O where x, y and z are integers. The distance OA is 9 m. Find the values of x, y and z.

1.5 The analysis of systems of forces

The simplest case of a system of forces acting on a rigid body arises when the forces all act through a common point. In such a case, the resultant of the forces is found by adding the forces.

Example 12

Forces $\mathbf{F}_1$, $\mathbf{F}_2$ and $\mathbf{F}_3$ where $\mathbf{F}_1 = (-3\mathbf{i} + 6\mathbf{j} + 7\mathbf{k})\,\mathrm{N}$, $\mathbf{F}_2 = (5\mathbf{i} + 7\mathbf{j} - 2\mathbf{k})\,\mathrm{N}$ and $\mathbf{F}_3 = (9\mathbf{i} - 5\mathbf{j} + 3\mathbf{k})\,\mathrm{N}$ all act at point P of a rigid body.

(a) Find the resultant of the three forces.

A fourth force $\mathbf{F}_4$, also acting through P, is to be introduced and the resulting system is to be in equilibrium.

(b) Find the force $\mathbf{F}_4$.

(a) Resultant $= \mathbf{F}_1 + \mathbf{F}_2 + \mathbf{F}_3$

$$= (-3\mathbf{i} + 6\mathbf{j} + 7\mathbf{k}) + (5\mathbf{i} + 7\mathbf{j} - 2\mathbf{k}) + (9\mathbf{i} - 5\mathbf{j} + 3\mathbf{k})$$

$$= 11\mathbf{i} + 8\mathbf{j} + 8\mathbf{k}$$

The resultant is $(11\mathbf{i} + 8\mathbf{j} + 8\mathbf{k})\,\text{N}$.

(b) For the new system to be in equilibrium,

$$\mathbf{F}_1 + \mathbf{F}_2 + \mathbf{F}_3 + \mathbf{F}_4 = \mathbf{0}$$

or: $$\mathbf{F}_4 = -(\mathbf{F}_1 + \mathbf{F}_2 + \mathbf{F}_3)$$

The new force $\mathbf{F}_4$ is $-(11\mathbf{i} + 8\mathbf{j} + 8\mathbf{k})\,\text{N}$.

Couples

When the forces acting on a body do not all act through the same point, it is possible for the sum of the forces to be zero, so there is no resultant force, although the sum of the moments of the separate forces about some point is not zero. To illustrate this, consider the case of a pair of forces $\mathbf{F}$ and $-\mathbf{F}$ acting on a body and having different lines of action. Such a pair will act in opposite directions along a pair of parallel lines as shown in the diagram:

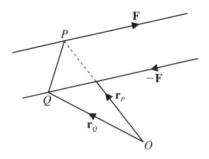

Let O be any fixed point which need not be in the plane of $\mathbf{F}$ and $-\mathbf{F}$. Let P and Q be any points on the lines of action of $\mathbf{F}$ and $-\mathbf{F}$ respectively, having position vectors $\mathbf{r}_P$ and $\mathbf{r}_Q$ relative to O. Then the vector moment of $\mathbf{F}$ about O is $\mathbf{r}_P \times \mathbf{F}$ and the vector moment of $-\mathbf{F}$ about O is $\mathbf{r}_Q \times (-\mathbf{F})$. The total vector moment about O of the system

$$= \mathbf{r}_P \times \mathbf{F} + \mathbf{r}_Q \times (-\mathbf{F})$$

$$= \mathbf{r}_P \times \mathbf{F} - \mathbf{r}_Q \times \mathbf{F}$$

$$= (\mathbf{r}_P - \mathbf{r}_Q) \times \mathbf{F}$$

$$= \overrightarrow{QP} \times \mathbf{F}$$

Thus the vector moment of the pair of forces is independent of the position of O. Consequently, the vector moment of the pair of forces is the same about any point. Such a pair of forces is called a **couple**.

Equivalent systems of forces

Two systems of forces are said to be **equivalent** if they have the same effect when applied to the same body. A system of coplanar forces must be equivalent to

(a) a single resultant force or

(b) to a couple or

(c) must be in equilibrium.

When forces in three dimensions are being considered, another possibility arises.

Poinsot's reduction of a system of forces

Consider a set of forces $\mathbf{F}_1, \mathbf{F}_2, \mathbf{F}_3, \ldots, \mathbf{F}_n$ acting on a body with their lines of action passing through the points with position vectors $\mathbf{r}_1, \mathbf{r}_2, \mathbf{r}_3, \ldots, \mathbf{r}_n$ relative to a fixed origin O. Corresponding to each force $\mathbf{F}_1, \mathbf{F}_2, \mathbf{F}_3, \ldots, \mathbf{F}_n$ introduce at O pairs of forces $\pm\mathbf{F}_1, \pm\mathbf{F}_2, \pm\mathbf{F}_3, \ldots, \pm\mathbf{F}_n$.

For a typical force $\mathbf{F}_i$ we have:

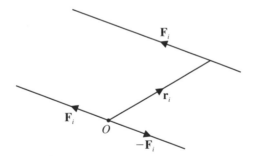

The resultant of the system of forces is unchanged by the addition of these pairs of forces. However, as can be seen from the diagram, the system now consists of a set of forces $\mathbf{F}_1, \mathbf{F}_2, \mathbf{F}_3, \ldots, \mathbf{F}_n$ acting at O together with a set of couples of moment

$$\mathbf{r}_1 \times \mathbf{F}_1, \mathbf{r}_2 \times \mathbf{F}_2, \mathbf{r}_3 \times \mathbf{F}_3, \ldots, \mathbf{r}_n \times \mathbf{F}_n.$$

Let the resultant of the forces $\mathbf{F}_1, \mathbf{F}_2, \mathbf{F}_3, \ldots, \mathbf{F}_n$ acting at O be $\mathbf{F}$.

Then: $$\mathbf{F} = \mathbf{F}_1 + \mathbf{F}_2 + \mathbf{F}_3 + \ldots + \mathbf{F}_n$$

or: $$\mathbf{F} = \sum_{i=1}^{n} \mathbf{F}_i$$

and the couples are equivalent to a single couple $\mathbf{G}$ where:

$$\mathbf{G} = \mathbf{r}_1 \times \mathbf{F}_1 + \mathbf{r}_2 \times \mathbf{F}_2 + \mathbf{r}_3 \times \mathbf{F}_3 + \ldots + \mathbf{r}_n \times \mathbf{F}_n$$

or:
$$\mathbf{G} = \sum_{i=1}^{n} \mathbf{r}_i \times \mathbf{F}_i$$

Thus:

- **A system of forces $\mathbf{F}_1, \mathbf{F}_2, \ldots, \mathbf{F}_n$ with lines of action passing through the points with position vectors $\mathbf{r}_1, \mathbf{r}_2, \ldots, \mathbf{r}_n$ relative to an origin O is equivalent to a single force $\mathbf{F} = \sum_{i=1}^{n} \mathbf{F}_i$ acting at O and a couple of moment $\mathbf{G} = \sum_{i=1}^{n} \mathbf{r}_i \times \mathbf{F}_i$.**

The resultant force $\mathbf{F}$ is the same, whatever point is taken to be the origin O. However, the moment of the couple changes if $\mathbf{F}$ is required to act at a point other than O. This can be seen by considering a system which reduces to a single force $\mathbf{F} = \sum_{i=1}^{n} \mathbf{F}_i$ at O and a couple of moment $\mathbf{G} = \sum_{i=1}^{n} \mathbf{r}_i \times \mathbf{F}_i$ about O.

Suppose instead that the resultant force is required to act through the point A with position vector $\mathbf{r}_A$ relative to O.

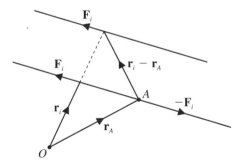

Pairs of forces $\pm\mathbf{F}_1, \pm\mathbf{F}_2, \ldots, \pm\mathbf{F}_n$ are introduced at A. This gives a set of forces $\mathbf{F}_1, \mathbf{F}_2, \ldots, \mathbf{F}_n$ acting at A, together with a set of couples of moment $(\mathbf{r}_1 - \mathbf{r}_A) \times \mathbf{F}_1, (\mathbf{r}_2 - \mathbf{r}_A) \times \mathbf{F}_2, \ldots (\mathbf{r}_n - \mathbf{r}_A) \times \mathbf{F}_n$.

Hence the resultant force $\mathbf{F}$ is given by:

$$\mathbf{F} = \mathbf{F}_1 + \mathbf{F}_2 + \mathbf{F}_3 + \ldots + \mathbf{F}_n$$

which is the same as before but now it is acting at A. However, the couple is now:

$$\sum_{i=1}^{n} (\mathbf{r}_i - \mathbf{r}_A) \times \mathbf{F}_i = \sum_{i=1}^{n} \mathbf{r}_i \times \mathbf{F}_i - \sum_{i=1}^{n} \mathbf{r}_A \times \mathbf{F}_i$$

$$= \mathbf{G} - \mathbf{r}_A \times \sum_{i=1}^{n} \mathbf{F}_i$$

$$= \mathbf{G} - \mathbf{r}_A \times \mathbf{F}$$

All systems of forces can be reduced to a single force $\mathbf{F}$ and a couple of moment $\mathbf{G}$. Different cases arise when either or both of $\mathbf{F}$ and $\mathbf{G}$ are the zero vector.

(a) When $\mathbf{F} = \mathbf{0}$ the system reduces to a couple.

(b) When $\mathbf{G} = \mathbf{0}$ the system reduces to a single force.

(c) When $\mathbf{F} = \mathbf{0}$ and $\mathbf{G} = \mathbf{0}$, the system is in equilibrium.

As the moment of the couple about the point A, with position vector $\mathbf{r}_A$ relative to O, is $\mathbf{G} - \mathbf{r}_A \times \mathbf{F}$ (see above) it follows that when both $\mathbf{F}$ and $\mathbf{G}$ are zero, the moment of the couple about the point A is also zero. Hence to prove a system is in equilibrium it is sufficient to show that:

(a) $\mathbf{F} = \mathbf{0}$

(b) the sum of the moments of the forces about *any* point is zero.

Alternatively, you can show that $\mathbf{F} = \mathbf{0}$ and the forces are concurrent, which implies a zero total moment about the common point.

Hence:

■   **A system of forces in three dimensions is either in equilibrium or can be reduced to a single force, a couple or a couple and a force.**

Example 13

A rigid body is in equilibrium under the action of four forces $\mathbf{F}_1$, $\mathbf{F}_2$, $\mathbf{F}_3$ and $\mathbf{F}_4$ acting at points with position vectors $\mathbf{r}_1$, $\mathbf{r}_2$, $\mathbf{r}_3$ and $\mathbf{r}_4$ relative to a fixed origin O, where:

$$\mathbf{F}_1 = (5\mathbf{i} + 2\mathbf{j} - \mathbf{k})\,\text{N} \qquad \mathbf{r}_1 = 4\mathbf{k}\,\text{m}$$

$$\mathbf{F}_2 = (3\mathbf{i} - 2\mathbf{j} - 2\mathbf{k})\,\text{N} \qquad \mathbf{r}_2 = (8\mathbf{i} + \mathbf{k})\,\text{m}$$

$$\mathbf{F}_3 = (-2\mathbf{i} + 3\mathbf{j} + 2\mathbf{k})\,\text{N} \qquad \mathbf{r}_3 = (\mathbf{i} + 8\mathbf{j} + 7\mathbf{k})\,\text{m}$$

Find $\mathbf{F}_4$ and an equation for the line of action of $\mathbf{F}_4$.

As the system is in equilibrium $\sum_i \mathbf{F}_i = \mathbf{0}$ and $\sum_i \mathbf{r}_i \times \mathbf{F}_i = \mathbf{0}$

So: $\qquad \mathbf{F}_1 + \mathbf{F}_2 + \mathbf{F}_3 + \mathbf{F}_4 = \mathbf{0}$

$$\begin{aligned} \mathbf{F}_4 &= -(\mathbf{F}_1 + \mathbf{F}_2 + \mathbf{F}_3) \\ &= -[(5\mathbf{i} + 2\mathbf{j} - \mathbf{k}) + (3\mathbf{i} - 2\mathbf{j} - 2\mathbf{k}) \\ &\quad + (-2\mathbf{i} + 3\mathbf{j} + 2\mathbf{k})] \\ &= -6\mathbf{i} - 3\mathbf{j} + \mathbf{k} \end{aligned}$$

So $\mathbf{F}_4$ is $(-6\mathbf{i} - 3\mathbf{j} + \mathbf{k})\,\mathrm{N}$.

The line of action of $\mathbf{F}_4$ is parallel to the vector $-6\mathbf{i} - 3\mathbf{j} + \mathbf{k}$ but to find its equation, the position vector $\mathbf{r}_4$, of a point on the line, is required.

Since $\qquad\qquad\qquad \sum_i \mathbf{r}_i \times \mathbf{F}_i = \mathbf{0}$

it follows that $\mathbf{r}_4 \times \mathbf{F}_4 = -[\mathbf{r}_1 \times \mathbf{F}_1 + \mathbf{r}_2 \times \mathbf{F}_2 + \mathbf{r}_3 \times \mathbf{F}_3]$

$$\mathbf{r}_1 \times \mathbf{F}_1 = \begin{vmatrix} \mathbf{i} & \mathbf{j} & \mathbf{k} \\ 0 & 0 & 4 \\ 5 & 2 & -1 \end{vmatrix} = -8\mathbf{i} + 20\mathbf{j}$$

$$\mathbf{r}_2 \times \mathbf{F}_2 = \begin{vmatrix} \mathbf{i} & \mathbf{j} & \mathbf{k} \\ 8 & 0 & 1 \\ 3 & -2 & -2 \end{vmatrix} = 2\mathbf{i} + 19\mathbf{j} - 16\mathbf{k}$$

$$\mathbf{r}_3 \times \mathbf{F}_3 = \begin{vmatrix} \mathbf{i} & \mathbf{j} & \mathbf{k} \\ 1 & 8 & 7 \\ -2 & 3 & 2 \end{vmatrix} = -5\mathbf{i} - 16\mathbf{j} + 19\mathbf{k}$$

So: $\qquad \mathbf{r}_1 \times \mathbf{F}_1 + \mathbf{r}_2 \times \mathbf{F}_2 + \mathbf{r}_3 \times \mathbf{F}_3 = -11\mathbf{i} + 23\mathbf{j} + 3\mathbf{k}$

And hence: $\qquad \mathbf{r}_4 \times \mathbf{F}_4 = -(-11\mathbf{i} + 23\mathbf{j} + 3\mathbf{k})$

$$= 11\mathbf{i} - 23\mathbf{j} - 3\mathbf{k} \qquad (1)$$

Let $\mathbf{r}_4 = x\mathbf{i} + y\mathbf{j} + z\mathbf{k}$

Then:

$$\mathbf{r}_4 \times \mathbf{F}_4 = \begin{vmatrix} \mathbf{i} & \mathbf{j} & \mathbf{k} \\ x & y & z \\ -6 & -3 & 1 \end{vmatrix}$$

$$= (y + 3z)\mathbf{i} - (x + 6z)\mathbf{j} + (-3x + 6y)\mathbf{k} \qquad (2)$$

Equating the coefficients of $\mathbf{i}, \mathbf{j}, \mathbf{k}$ in equations (1) and (2) gives:

$$(y + 3z) = 11 \qquad (3)$$

$$-(x + 6z) = -23 \qquad (4)$$

$$(-3x + 6y) = -3 \qquad (5)$$

Note that these equations do not have a unique solution as (x, y, z) are the coordinates of *any* point on the line of action of $\mathbf{F}_4$.

In particular, take $x = 0$.

Then from equation (4), $z = \frac{23}{6}$

And from equation (5) $y = -\frac{1}{2}$

(These values of y and z also satisfy equation (3). If they did not, the system would not be in equilibrium or the line of action of $\mathbf{F}_4$ would not intersect the plane $x = 0$.)

Since the line of action of $\mathbf{F}_4$ is parallel to the vector $-6\mathbf{i} - 3\mathbf{j} + \mathbf{k}$ and passes through the point with position vector $-\frac{1}{2}\mathbf{j} + \frac{23}{6}\mathbf{k}$ it has equation:

$$\mathbf{r} = -\tfrac{1}{2}\mathbf{j} + \tfrac{23}{6}\mathbf{k} + \lambda(-6\mathbf{i} - 3\mathbf{j} + \mathbf{k})$$

Example 14

Forces $\mathbf{F}_1$, $\mathbf{F}_2$ and $\mathbf{F}_3$ act on a body at points with position vectors $\mathbf{r}_1$, $\mathbf{r}_2$, $\mathbf{r}_3$ relative to a fixed origin O, where:

$$\mathbf{F}_1 = (2\mathbf{i} + 3\mathbf{j} + 4\mathbf{k})\,\text{N} \qquad \mathbf{r}_1 = (-\mathbf{i} + 2\mathbf{j} + \mathbf{k})\,\text{m}$$
$$\mathbf{F}_2 = (4\mathbf{i} - 3\mathbf{j} + 2\mathbf{k})\,\text{N} \qquad \mathbf{r}_2 = (3\mathbf{i} - 3\mathbf{j})\,\text{m}$$
$$\mathbf{F}_3 = (-3\mathbf{i} + 2\mathbf{j} - \mathbf{k})\,\text{N} \qquad \mathbf{r}_3 = (4\mathbf{i} + 2\mathbf{k})\,\text{m}$$

This system can be reduced to a single force $\mathbf{F}$ acting at point A with position vector $\mathbf{r}_A = (\mathbf{i} + \mathbf{j} + \mathbf{k})$ together with a couple $\mathbf{G}$.

  (a) Find the force $\mathbf{F}$ and the couple $\mathbf{G}$.
  (b) Give, in vector form, an equation for the line of action of $\mathbf{F}$.

(a) $\mathbf{F} = \displaystyle\sum_i \mathbf{F}_i$

$\qquad = (2\mathbf{i} + 3\mathbf{j} + 4\mathbf{k}) + (4\mathbf{i} - 3\mathbf{j} + 2\mathbf{k}) + (-3\mathbf{i} + 2\mathbf{j} - \mathbf{k})$

$\qquad = 3\mathbf{i} + 2\mathbf{j} + 5\mathbf{k}.$

Take moments about A:

moment of $\mathbf{F}_i = (\mathbf{r}_i - \mathbf{r}_A) \times \mathbf{F}_i$

$$\text{moment of } \mathbf{F}_1 = \begin{vmatrix} \mathbf{i} & \mathbf{j} & \mathbf{k} \\ -2 & 1 & 0 \\ 2 & 3 & 4 \end{vmatrix} = 4\mathbf{i} + 8\mathbf{j} - 8\mathbf{k}$$

$$\text{moment of } \mathbf{F}_2 = \begin{vmatrix} \mathbf{i} & \mathbf{j} & \mathbf{k} \\ 2 & -4 & -1 \\ 4 & -3 & 2 \end{vmatrix} = -11\mathbf{i} - 8\mathbf{j} + 10\mathbf{k}$$

$$\text{moment of } \mathbf{F}_3 = \begin{vmatrix} \mathbf{i} & \mathbf{j} & \mathbf{k} \\ 3 & -1 & 1 \\ -3 & 2 & -1 \end{vmatrix} = -\mathbf{i} + 3\mathbf{k}$$

So:
$$\mathbf{G} = \sum_i (\mathbf{r}_i - \mathbf{r}_A) \times \mathbf{F}_i$$
$$= (4\mathbf{i} + 8\mathbf{j} - 8\mathbf{k}) + (-11\mathbf{i} - 8\mathbf{j} + 10\mathbf{k}) + (-\mathbf{i} + 3\mathbf{k})$$
$$= -8\mathbf{i} + 5\mathbf{k}$$

The force is $(3\mathbf{i} + 2\mathbf{j} + 5\mathbf{k})\,\mathrm{N}$ and the couple is $(-8\mathbf{i} + 5\mathbf{k})\,\mathrm{Nm}$.

(b) The line of action of $\mathbf{F}$ is parallel to $(3\mathbf{i} + 2\mathbf{j} + 5\mathbf{k})$ and passes through A where $\mathbf{r}_A = \mathbf{i} + \mathbf{j} + \mathbf{k}$.

An equation for the line of action of $\mathbf{F}$ is therefore:
$$\mathbf{r} = \mathbf{i} + \mathbf{j} + \mathbf{k} + \lambda(3\mathbf{i} + 2\mathbf{j} + 5\mathbf{k})$$

Example 15

Three forces $\mathbf{F}_1$, $\mathbf{F}_2$ and $\mathbf{F}_3$ act on a rigid body at points having position vectors $\mathbf{r}_1$, $\mathbf{r}_2$ and $\mathbf{r}_3$ relative to a fixed origin O where:

$$\mathbf{F}_1 = (-3\mathbf{i} - 2\mathbf{j} + 4\mathbf{k})\,\mathrm{N} \qquad \mathbf{r}_1 = (2\mathbf{i} + 4\mathbf{j} - \mathbf{k})\,\mathrm{m}$$
$$\mathbf{F}_2 = (5\mathbf{i} + 3\mathbf{j} - 7\mathbf{k})\,\mathrm{N} \qquad \mathbf{r}_2 = (\mathbf{i} - \mathbf{j} - \mathbf{k})\,\mathrm{m}$$
$$\mathbf{F}_3 = (-2\mathbf{i} - \mathbf{j} + 3\mathbf{k})\,\mathrm{N} \qquad \mathbf{r}_3 = (2\mathbf{i} + 3\mathbf{k})\,\mathrm{m}$$

Show that the system reduces to a couple and find the magnitude of the couple.

If the system reduces to a couple, $\sum_i \mathbf{F}_i = \mathbf{0}$.

$$\sum_i \mathbf{F}_i = (-3\mathbf{i} - 2\mathbf{j} + 4\mathbf{k}) + (5\mathbf{i} + 3\mathbf{j} - 7\mathbf{k}) + (-2\mathbf{i} - \mathbf{j} + 3\mathbf{k}) = \mathbf{0}$$

So the system is either in equilibrium or reduces to a couple. To ascertain which of these is the case, the moments of the forces about O must be calculated.

$$\text{moment of } \mathbf{F}_1 = \mathbf{r}_1 \times \mathbf{F}_1 = \begin{vmatrix} \mathbf{i} & \mathbf{j} & \mathbf{k} \\ 2 & 4 & -1 \\ -3 & -2 & 4 \end{vmatrix} = 14\mathbf{i} - 5\mathbf{j} + 8\mathbf{k}$$

$$\text{moment of } \mathbf{F}_2 = \mathbf{r}_2 \times \mathbf{F}_2 = \begin{vmatrix} \mathbf{i} & \mathbf{j} & \mathbf{k} \\ 1 & -1 & -1 \\ 5 & 3 & -7 \end{vmatrix} = 10\mathbf{i} + 2\mathbf{j} + 8\mathbf{k}$$

$$\text{moment of } \mathbf{F}_3 = \mathbf{r}_3 \times \mathbf{F}_3 = \begin{vmatrix} \mathbf{i} & \mathbf{j} & \mathbf{k} \\ 2 & 0 & 3 \\ -2 & -1 & 3 \end{vmatrix} = 3\mathbf{i} - 12\mathbf{j} - 2\mathbf{k}$$

So:

$$\sum_i \mathbf{r}_i \times \mathbf{F}_i = (14\mathbf{i} - 5\mathbf{j} + 8\mathbf{k}) + (10\mathbf{i} + 2\mathbf{j} + 8\mathbf{k}) + (3\mathbf{i} - 12\mathbf{j} - 2\mathbf{k})$$
$$= 27\mathbf{i} - 15\mathbf{j} + 14\mathbf{k}$$

As $\sum_i \mathbf{r}_i \times \mathbf{F}_i \neq \mathbf{0}$, the system reduces to a couple of magnitude

$(27\mathbf{i} - 15\mathbf{j} + 14\mathbf{k})$ Nm.

Exercise 1D

1 Forces $\mathbf{F}_1, \mathbf{F}_2, \mathbf{F}_3$ and $\mathbf{F}_4$ act on a particle. Find the resultant of the forces in each of the following cases:

   (a) $\mathbf{F}_1 = (5\mathbf{i} + 2\mathbf{j} - 3\mathbf{k})$ N, $\mathbf{F}_2 = (3\mathbf{i} - 7\mathbf{k})$ N,
        $\mathbf{F}_3 = (-6\mathbf{i} + 2\mathbf{j} + 3\mathbf{k})$ N, $\mathbf{F}_4 = (4\mathbf{i} + 2\mathbf{k})$ N

   (b) $\mathbf{F}_1 = (9\mathbf{i} + 7\mathbf{j} - 3\mathbf{k})$ N, $\mathbf{F}_2 = (4\mathbf{i} - 3\mathbf{j} + 5\mathbf{k})$ N,
        $\mathbf{F}_3 = (-3\mathbf{i} + 2\mathbf{j} - \mathbf{k})$ N, $\mathbf{F}_4 = (3\mathbf{i} - 2\mathbf{j} + \mathbf{k})$ N.

2 A particle is in equilibrium under the action of four forces $\mathbf{F}_1$, $\mathbf{F}_2, \mathbf{F}_3$ and $\mathbf{F}_4$. Find $\mathbf{F}_4$ when $\mathbf{F}_1, \mathbf{F}_2$, and $\mathbf{F}_3$ are as given:

   (a) $\mathbf{F}_1 = (2\mathbf{i} - 3\mathbf{j})$ N, $\mathbf{F}_2 = (5\mathbf{i} + 7\mathbf{j})$ N, $\mathbf{F}_3 = (-3\mathbf{i} + \mathbf{j})$ N

   (b) $\mathbf{F}_1 = (6\mathbf{i} + 2\mathbf{j} + \mathbf{k})$ N, $\mathbf{F}_2 = (4\mathbf{i} + 3\mathbf{j} - 6\mathbf{k})$ N, $\mathbf{F}_3 = (-\mathbf{i} - 2\mathbf{j} + 2\mathbf{k})$ N

   (c) $\mathbf{F}_1 = (-9\mathbf{i} + 7\mathbf{j} + 5\mathbf{k})$ N, $\mathbf{F}_2 = (5\mathbf{i} - 3\mathbf{j} - \mathbf{k})$ N, $\mathbf{F}_3 = (6\mathbf{i} - \mathbf{j} + 3\mathbf{k})$ N

3 Four forces $\mathbf{F}_1, \mathbf{F}_2, \mathbf{F}_3$ and $\mathbf{F}_4$ act at points of a rigid body with position vectors $\mathbf{r}_1, \mathbf{r}_2, \mathbf{r}_3$ and $\mathbf{r}_4$ respectively relative to a fixed origin where:

   $\mathbf{F}_1 = (3\mathbf{i} - 4\mathbf{j} + 5\mathbf{k})$ N, $\mathbf{r}_1 = (4\mathbf{i} - 2\mathbf{j} + 6\mathbf{k})$ m

   $\mathbf{F}_2 = (2\mathbf{i} + 6\mathbf{j} - 3\mathbf{k})$ N, $\mathbf{r}_2 = (3\mathbf{i} + 8\mathbf{j} - 2\mathbf{k})$ m

   $\mathbf{F}_3 = (-6\mathbf{i} + 2\mathbf{j} + 2\mathbf{k})$ N, $\mathbf{r}_3 = (7\mathbf{i} - \mathbf{k})$ m

   $\mathbf{F}_4 = (\mathbf{i} - 4\mathbf{j} - 4\mathbf{k})$ N, $\mathbf{r}_4 = (6\mathbf{j} + 5\mathbf{k})$ m

   Show that the body is in equilibrium.

4 Forces $\mathbf{F}_1, \mathbf{F}_2$, and $\mathbf{F}_3$ act at points of a body with position vectors $\mathbf{r}_1, \mathbf{r}_2$, and $\mathbf{r}_3$ relative to a fixed origin, where:

   $\mathbf{F}_1 = (3\mathbf{i} - 3\mathbf{j} + 4\mathbf{k})$ N, $\mathbf{r}_1 = (\mathbf{i} + \mathbf{j} + \mathbf{k})$ m

   $\mathbf{F}_2 = (3\mathbf{i} + 4\mathbf{j} + 3\mathbf{k})$ N, $\mathbf{r}_2 = (3\mathbf{i} + 2\mathbf{j} + \mathbf{k})$ m

   $\mathbf{F}_3 = (-4\mathbf{i} - 2\mathbf{j} + \mathbf{k})$ N, $\mathbf{r}_3 = (2\mathbf{i} - \mathbf{j})$ m

(a) Reduce the system to a single force acting at the origin together with a couple.

(b) Reduce the system to a single force acting at the point with position vector $(\mathbf{i} - \mathbf{j} + 2\mathbf{k})\,\mathrm{m}$ together with a couple.

(c) In each case, state in vector form an equation for the line of action of the force.

5 Forces $\mathbf{F}_1$, $\mathbf{F}_2$ and $\mathbf{F}_3$ act on a rigid body at points having position vectors $\mathbf{r}_1$, $\mathbf{r}_2$ and $\mathbf{r}_3$ relative to a fixed origin O where:

$\mathbf{F}_1 = (4\mathbf{i} - 2\mathbf{j} + 2\mathbf{k})\,\mathrm{N},$ $\mathbf{r}_1 = (\mathbf{i} + 4\mathbf{j} - 2\mathbf{k})\,\mathrm{m}$

$\mathbf{F}_2 = (-2\mathbf{i} - 3\mathbf{j} - 6\mathbf{k})\,\mathrm{N},$ $\mathbf{r}_2 = (2\mathbf{i} - 2\mathbf{j} - 2\mathbf{k})\,\mathrm{m}$

$\mathbf{F}_3 = (-2\mathbf{i} + 5\mathbf{j} + 4\mathbf{k})\,\mathrm{N},$ $\mathbf{r}_3 = (3\mathbf{i} + 2\mathbf{k})\,\mathrm{m}$

Show that the system reduces to a couple.

6 Forces $\mathbf{F}_1$, $\mathbf{F}_2$ and $\mathbf{F}_3$ of magnitudes $14\,\mathrm{N}$, $15\,\mathrm{N}$ and $9\,\mathrm{N}$ act on a body through the points with position vectors $(3\mathbf{i} + 4\mathbf{j} - 2\mathbf{k})\,\mathrm{m}$, $(2\mathbf{i} + 3\mathbf{j} + 4\mathbf{k})\,\mathrm{m}$ and $(-2\mathbf{i} + \mathbf{j} + \mathbf{k})\,\mathrm{m}$.

$\mathbf{F}_1$ acts parallel to $2\mathbf{i} + 3\mathbf{j} + 6\mathbf{k}$.

$\mathbf{F}_2$ acts parallel to $3\mathbf{i} + 4\mathbf{j}$.

$\mathbf{F}_3$ acts parallel to $-8\mathbf{i} + 4\mathbf{j} - \mathbf{k}$.

Reduce the system to a single force $\mathbf{F}_4$ acting at the point with position vector $(2\mathbf{i} - 2\mathbf{j} + 4\mathbf{k})$ together with a couple.

7 Forces $\mathbf{F}_1$, $\mathbf{F}_2$ and $\mathbf{F}_3$ act on a rigid body at the points with position vectors $\mathbf{r}_1$, $\mathbf{r}_2$ and $\mathbf{r}_3$ relative to a fixed origin O where:

$\mathbf{F}_1 = (3\mathbf{i} - 2\mathbf{j} + \mathbf{k})\,\mathrm{N},$ $\mathbf{r}_1 = (7\mathbf{i} + 6\mathbf{j})\,\mathrm{m}$

$\mathbf{F}_2 = (4\mathbf{i} + 7\mathbf{j} + 2\mathbf{k})\,\mathrm{N},$ $\mathbf{r}_2 = (-\mathbf{i} - 8\mathbf{j} - 4\mathbf{k})\,\mathrm{m}$

$\mathbf{F}_3 = (2\mathbf{i} - \mathbf{j} + 3\mathbf{k})\,\mathrm{N},$ $\mathbf{r}_3 = (5\mathbf{i} + 7\mathbf{j} - 3\mathbf{k})\,\mathrm{m}.$

Show that the three forces can be reduced to a single force $\mathbf{R}$. Find a vector equation for the line of action of $\mathbf{R}$.

8 Four forces $(-\mathbf{i} - \mathbf{j} + \mathbf{k})\,\mathrm{N}$, $(2\mathbf{i} - \mathbf{k})\,\mathrm{N}$, $(\mathbf{i} + \mathbf{j} + \mathbf{k})\,\mathrm{N}$ and $\mathbf{F}$ act on a rigid body at the points with position vectors $(-10\mathbf{i} + 2\mathbf{j})\,\mathrm{m}$, $6\mathbf{j}\,\mathrm{m}$, $3\mathbf{k}\,\mathrm{m}$ and $(2\mathbf{i} + 3\mathbf{k})\,\mathrm{m}$ relative to a fixed origin. The four forces are equivalent to a couple. Find

(a) the force $\mathbf{F}$

(b) the magnitude of the couple $\mathbf{G}$,

stating your units clearly.

SUMMARY OF KEY POINTS

1 The position vector of A relative to B, $_A\mathbf{r}_B$, is given by:

$$_A\mathbf{r}_B = \mathbf{r}_A - \mathbf{r}_B$$

where $\mathbf{r}_A$ and $\mathbf{r}_B$ are the position vectors of A and B relative to a fixed origin.

2 Two moving particles A and B collide if at some time $_A\mathbf{r}_B = \mathbf{0}$.

3 The velocity of A relative to B, $_A\mathbf{v}_B$, is given by:

$$_A\mathbf{v}_B = \mathbf{v}_A - \mathbf{v}_B$$

where $\mathbf{v}_A$ and $\mathbf{v}_B$ are the actual velocities of A and B.

4 Two particles A and B are closest together when $|_A\mathbf{r}_B|$ has a minimum value. This minimum can be found by differentiating $|_A\mathbf{r}_B|^2$ with respect to time.

5 Alternatively, $|_A\mathbf{r}_B|$ is a minimum when $_A\mathbf{r}_B._A\mathbf{v}_B = 0$.

6 To solve a vector differential equation of the type $\dfrac{\mathrm{d}\mathbf{v}}{\mathrm{d}t} = k\mathbf{v}$

substitute: $\mathbf{v} = u\mathbf{i} + w\mathbf{j}$ (2 dimensions)
or: $\mathbf{v} = u\mathbf{i} + w\mathbf{j} + s\mathbf{k}$ (3 dimensions)
and solve the resulting scalar equations.

7 The vector differential equation

$$\frac{\mathrm{d}^2\mathbf{r}}{\mathrm{d}t^2} + 2k\frac{\mathrm{d}\mathbf{r}}{\mathrm{d}t} + (k^2 + n^2)\mathbf{r} = \mathbf{0}$$

should also be solved by substitution, as in key point 6.

8 The vector differential equation $\dfrac{\mathrm{d}\mathbf{r}}{\mathrm{d}t} + \mathrm{f}(t)\mathbf{r} = \mathbf{a}\mathrm{e}^{bt}$ must first be multiplied by the integrating factor $\mathrm{e}^{\int \mathrm{f}(t)\mathrm{d}t}$. It can then be integrated directly, without any substitution.

9 The work done by a constant force $\mathbf{F}$ which moves its point of application through a displacement $\mathbf{d}$ is given by:

$$\text{Work done} = \mathbf{F}.\mathbf{d}$$

10 The vector moment of the force $\mathbf{F}$ about the origin O is given by:

$$\text{Vector moment of force} = \mathbf{r} \times \mathbf{F},$$

where $\mathbf{r}$ is the position vector, relative to O, of any point on the line of action of $\mathbf{F}$.

11 A system of forces $\mathbf{F}_1$, $\mathbf{F}_2, \ldots, \mathbf{F}_n$ with lines of action passing through the points with position vectors $\mathbf{r}_1$, $\mathbf{r}_2, \ldots \mathbf{r}_n$ relative to an origin O, is equivalent to a single force

$$\mathbf{F} = \sum_{i=1}^{n} \mathbf{F}_i \quad \text{acting at } O \text{ and a couple of moment}$$

$$\mathbf{G} = \sum_{i=1}^{n} \mathbf{r}_i \times \mathbf{F}_i.$$

12 If the resultant force $\mathbf{F}$ is required to act at some point other than O, $\mathbf{F}$ is unchanged but the couple will have a different moment.

13 A system of forces is in equilibrium if $\mathbf{F} = \mathbf{0}$ and the sum of the moments of the forces about any point is zero.

14 A system of forces in three dimensions is either in equilibrium or can be reduced to a single force, a couple, or a force and a couple.

Kinematics of a particle moving in two dimensions

2

The earlier books in this series M1, M2 and M3, looked at the velocity and acceleration of a particle P moving on a straight line or on a circular path. This chapter considers these quantities when a particle P moves along a general curve in a plane.

In chapter 4 of Book P1, the use of rectangular cartesian coordinates to specify the position of a point in a plane was discussed. More generally the position of a particle P, in a plane, at any time, is specified by a pair of coordinates, which together define the position vector of P. Each of these coordinates is a function of the time t. The two equations for the coordinates in terms of t form parametric equations (see chapter 10 of Book P2) for the path of the particle.

This chapter looks at three of the coordinate systems available:

(1) cartesian coordinates (x, y)
(2) polar coordinates (r, θ)
(3) intrinsic coordinates (s, ψ).

Since velocity and acceleration are vector quantities it will be necessary in each case to find formulae for two components in specified directions whose sum is the vector required.

2.1 Velocity and acceleration components using cartesian coordinates

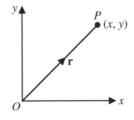

If at time t the particle P has cartesian coordinates x and y then its position vector is:

$$\mathbf{r} = x\mathbf{i} + y\mathbf{j}.$$

Its velocity is then:

$$\mathbf{v} = \dot{\mathbf{r}} = \dot{x}\mathbf{i} + \dot{y}\mathbf{j}$$

and its acceleration is:

$$\mathbf{f} = \dot{\mathbf{v}} = \ddot{\mathbf{r}} = \ddot{x}\mathbf{i} + \ddot{y}\mathbf{j}.$$

Example 1

A particle P moves round a circle centre O, radius a, so that OP has constant angular speed ω. Show that the velocity of P is along the tangent to its path and that its acceleration is along PO.

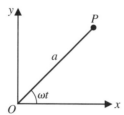

The diagram shows the position of P at time t with $\angle xOP = \theta = \omega t$. Taking O as the origin of cartesian coordinates:

$$x = a\cos\omega t, \qquad y = a\sin\omega t$$

and:
$$\mathbf{r} = \mathbf{i}a\cos\omega t + \mathbf{j}a\sin\omega t. \qquad (1)$$

The velocity $\mathbf{v}$ is obtained by differentiating (1) with respect to t. Hence:

$$\mathbf{v} = \omega[-\mathbf{i}a\sin\omega t + \mathbf{j}a\cos\omega t] \qquad (2)$$

$$= \omega\left[\mathbf{i}\cos\left(\omega t + \frac{\pi}{2}\right) + \mathbf{j}\sin\left(\omega t + \frac{\pi}{2}\right)\right]$$

which is a vector along the tangent to the circle.

Alternatively, taking the scalar product of equations (1) and (2) gives:

$$\mathbf{v}.\mathbf{r} = -\omega a^2\sin\omega t\cos\omega t + \omega a^2\sin\omega t\cos\omega t$$

$$= 0$$

This also shows that $\mathbf{v}$ is along the tangent as it is perpendicular to the position vector.

The acceleration is obtained by differentiating equation (2):

$$\mathbf{a} = \omega^2(-\mathbf{i}a\cos\omega t - \mathbf{j}a\sin\omega t)$$

$$= -\omega^2\mathbf{r}$$

Hence the acceleration is along PO since it is $(-\omega^2) \times$ the position vector of P relative to O.

Example 2

A particle P moves in a plane. Its acceleration is always directed towards a fixed point O of the plane and is of magnitude $n^2 \, (OP)$. The particle starts from rest at the point A where $OA = a$. Its initial velocity is perpendicular to OA and of magnitude nb. Obtain the parametric and cartesian equations of its path.

Take O as the origin and OA as the x-axis.

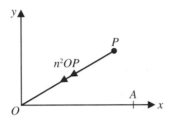

We have:
$$\mathbf{f} = \ddot{x}\mathbf{i} + \ddot{y}\mathbf{j} = -n^2(x\mathbf{i} + y\mathbf{j}) \tag{1}$$

So:
$$\ddot{x} = -n^2 x \tag{2}$$

$$\ddot{y} = -n^2 y \tag{3}$$

The general solution of equation (2), which is the simple harmonic equation, is:
$$x = A \cos nt + B \sin nt$$

But $x = a$ when $t = 0$ so $A = a$.
Also $\dot{x} = -An \sin nt + Bn \cos nt$ and $\dot{x} = 0$ when $t = 0$, so $B = 0$.

Hence:
$$x = a \cos nt \tag{4}$$

The general solution of (3) is:
$$y = \alpha \cos nt + \beta \sin nt.$$

But $y = 0$ and $\dot{y} = nb$.
So $\alpha = 0$ and $\beta = b$

and:
$$y = b \sin nt \tag{5}$$

Hence the parametric equation of the path of P is
$$x = a \cos nt, \; y = b \sin nt.$$

Since:
$$\sin^2 nt + \cos^2 nt = 1$$

$$\frac{x^2}{a^2} + \frac{y^2}{b^2} = 1$$

This is the cartesian equation of the path of P, which is an ellipse.

2.2 Differentiation of unit vectors in two dimensions

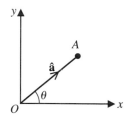

Let $\hat{\mathbf{a}}$ be a unit vector in the plane and $\mathbf{i}$ and $\mathbf{j}$ be the usual unit vectors along Ox and Oy respectively. Then if $\angle xOA = \theta$

$$\hat{\mathbf{a}} = \mathbf{i} \cos \theta + \mathbf{j} \sin \theta \qquad (1)$$

Differentiating with respect to time t gives:

$$\frac{\mathrm{d}\hat{\mathbf{a}}}{\mathrm{d}t} = \mathbf{i}(-\sin \theta \dot{\theta}) + \mathbf{j}(\cos \theta \dot{\theta})$$

as $\mathbf{i}$ and $\mathbf{j}$ are fixed in direction as well as being of unit length.

Since $\cos\left(\theta + \dfrac{\pi}{2}\right) = -\sin \theta$ and $\sin\left(\theta + \dfrac{\pi}{2}\right) = \cos \theta$ we can write

this equation in the form:

$$\frac{\mathrm{d}\hat{\mathbf{a}}}{\mathrm{d}t} = \dot{\theta}\hat{\mathbf{b}} \qquad (2)$$

where $\hat{\mathbf{b}} = \mathbf{i} \cos\left(\theta + \dfrac{\pi}{2}\right) + \mathbf{j} \sin\left(\theta + \dfrac{\pi}{2}\right)$

Therefore $\hat{\mathbf{b}}$ is a unit vector obtained by rotating $\hat{\mathbf{a}}$ through one right angle in the positive direction.

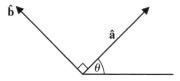

If $\mathbf{k}$ is a unit vector perpendicular to the plane of $\mathbf{i}$ and $\mathbf{j}$ and forms with them a right-handed set, then equation (2) can also be written:

$$\frac{\mathrm{d}\hat{\mathbf{a}}}{\mathrm{d}t} = \dot{\theta}(\mathbf{k} \times \hat{\mathbf{a}})$$

Note that since $\hat{\mathbf{b}} = -\mathbf{i} \sin \theta + \mathbf{j} \cos \theta$ then:

$$\frac{\mathrm{d}\hat{\mathbf{b}}}{\mathrm{d}t} = -\mathbf{i}\dot{\theta} \cos \theta - \mathbf{j}\dot{\theta} \sin \theta$$

$$= -\dot{\theta}\hat{\mathbf{a}} \qquad (3)$$

2.3 Velocity and acceleration components using polar coordinates

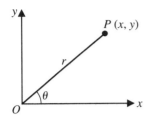 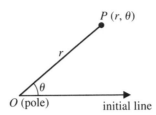

An alternative method of specifying the position of a point in a plane is to use polar coordinates (r, θ) (see Book P4 chapter 1), where r is the distance from a fixed point O, called the **pole** and θ is the angle made by OP with a fixed line through O, called the **initial line** as shown in the diagram.

In terms of these coordinates, the position vector of P may be written:

$$\overrightarrow{OP} = \mathbf{r} = r\mathbf{e}_r \tag{4}$$

where $\mathbf{e}_r$ is the unit vector in the direction OP.

Differentiating (4) with respect to time gives:

$$\mathbf{v} = \dot{\mathbf{r}} = \frac{\mathrm{d}r}{\mathrm{d}t}\mathbf{e}_r + r\frac{\mathrm{d}\mathbf{e}_r}{\mathrm{d}t}$$

and using equation (2) from section 2.2:

$$\frac{\mathrm{d}\mathbf{e}_r}{\mathrm{d}t} = \dot{\theta}\mathbf{e}_\theta$$

$$\mathbf{v} = \dot{r}\mathbf{e}_r + r\dot{\theta}\mathbf{e}_\theta \tag{5}$$

Hence:

- the **radial component** of the velocity is $\dot{r}$ and the **transverse component** of the velocity is $r\dot{\theta}$.

Velocity components in polar coordinates

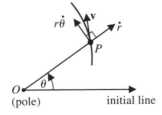

The acceleration is obtained by differentiating equation (5).

So:
$$\mathbf{f} = \dot{\mathbf{v}} = \ddot{r}\mathbf{e}_r + \dot{r}\frac{d\mathbf{e}_r}{dt} + (\dot{r}\dot{\theta} + r\ddot{\theta})\mathbf{e}_\theta + r\dot{\theta}\frac{d\mathbf{e}_\theta}{dt}$$

Using equations (2) and (3) from section 2.2 gives:

$$\mathbf{f} = \left(\ddot{r} - r\dot{\theta}^2\right)\mathbf{e}_r + \left(2\dot{r}\dot{\theta} + r\ddot{\theta}\right)\mathbf{e}_\theta \qquad (6)$$

Hence:

- the **radial component** of the acceleration is $(\ddot{r} - r\dot{\theta}^2)$, and the **transverse component** of the acceleration is:

$$(2\dot{r}\dot{\theta} + r\ddot{\theta}) = \frac{1}{r}\frac{d}{dt}(r^2\dot{\theta})$$

Acceleration components in polar coordinates

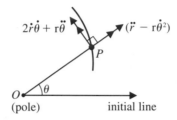

Example 3

A particle P describes the curve with polar equation $r = a\sin 2\theta$ in such a manner that the radius vector from the origin (pole) rotates with uniform angular speed ω. Find, in terms of ω, expressions for the radial and transverse components of the acceleration of the particle when $\theta = \dfrac{\pi}{4}$.

Since:
$$r = a\sin 2\theta$$
$$\dot{r} = a\dot{\theta}\, 2\cos 2\theta$$

But $\dot{\theta} = \omega$

so:
$$\dot{r} = 2a\omega\cos 2\theta$$

Differentiating again with respect to t gives:
$$\ddot{r} = 2a\omega(-2)\sin 2\theta \times \dot{\theta}$$
$$= -4a\omega^2\sin 2\theta$$

The radial component of the acceleration of P is:
$$\ddot{r} - r\dot{\theta}^2 = -4a\omega^2\sin 2\theta - a\sin 2\theta \times \omega^2$$
$$= -5a\omega^2\sin 2\theta$$

The transverse component of the acceleration of P is:
$$2\dot{r}\dot{\theta} + r\ddot{\theta} = 2(2a\omega\cos 2\theta)\omega + 0$$
$$= 4a\omega^2\cos 2\theta$$

as $\ddot{\theta} = 0$ ($\dot{\theta} = \omega$ which is constant).

When $\theta = \dfrac{\pi}{4}$:

$$\text{radial component} = -5a\omega^2$$

$$\text{transverse component} = 0$$

The acceleration is therefore purely radial and towards O, the pole.

Example 4

A particle moves along the curve with polar equation $r\theta = a \left(\theta \geqslant \dfrac{\pi}{4} \right)$ in such a way that the transverse component of the acceleration is always zero. Show that the radial component of acceleration is inversely proportional to r^3.

Since we are given that the transverse component of the acceleration is zero we have:

$$\frac{\mathrm{d}}{\mathrm{d}t} (r^2 \dot\theta) = 0$$

This form of the equation is used here as it is immediately integrable to give:

$$r^2 \dot\theta = k \tag{1}$$

where k is a constant.

Differentiating the equation of the curve, in the form $r = \dfrac{a}{\theta}$, gives:

$$\dot r = -\frac{a}{\theta^2} \dot\theta$$

Substituting $\dot\theta = \dfrac{k}{r^2}$ from (1) gives:

$$\dot r = -\frac{ak}{\theta^2 r^2}$$

But $r^2 \theta^2 = a^2$, from the equation of the curve,

so: $$\dot r = -\frac{ak}{a^2} = -\frac{k}{a}$$

which is constant.

Therefore $\ddot r = 0$.

The radial component of the acceleration is then:

$$\ddot r - r\dot\theta^2 = 0 - \frac{a}{\theta}\left(\frac{k}{r^2}\right)^2 = -\frac{ak^2}{r^4 \theta}$$

Substituting $\theta = \dfrac{a}{r}$ gives:

$$\ddot r = -\frac{ak^2}{r^3 a} = -\frac{k^2}{r^3}$$

So the radial acceleration is inversely proportional to r^3 as required.

Example 5

A particle P moves in a plane. At time t seconds its polar coordinates (r, θ), relative to a fixed origin O, are given by:

$$r = 2at, \quad \theta = t^2 - t$$

where a is a positive constant. Find the speed of P when $t = 2$.

To obtain the speed of P, the radial and transverse components of the velocity of P are required.

Since $r = 2at$ the radial velocity is:

$$\dot{r} = 2a$$

In this case $\dot{\theta} = 2t - 1$ and so when $t = 2$, $\dot{\theta} = 3$ and $r = 2a \times 2 = 4a$.

So the transverse velocity $r\dot{\theta} = (4a)(3) = 12a$.

The speed of P is:

$$\left[(2a)^2 + (12a)^2\right]^{\frac{1}{2}} = \left[4a^2 + 144a^2\right]^{\frac{1}{2}}$$
$$= a[148]^{\frac{1}{2}} = 2a\sqrt{37}$$

2.4 Velocity and acceleration components using intrinsic coordinates

Intrinsic coordinates are particularly useful when a particle P moves in a plane along a curve. One of the intrinsic coordinates is the arc length s along the curve from some fixed point to P and the other is the angle ψ between the tangent and a fixed direction (see Book P4 chapter 1).

The direction of the tangent at P will be denoted by the unit vector $\hat{\mathbf{s}}$ and the unit vector obtained from $\hat{\mathbf{s}}$ by rotating through $\frac{\pi}{2}$ in the positive sense will be denoted by $\hat{\mathbf{n}}$.

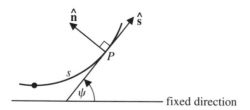

In the differential geometry of plane curves, the sign convention adopted is that the positive direction of the tangent is that in which the arc length is measured. The angle ψ is measured anti-clockwise from the x-axis to the positive tangent.

From the differentiation of unit vectors discussed earlier in this chapter, we have:

$$\frac{d\hat{\mathbf{s}}}{dt} = \dot{\psi}\hat{\mathbf{n}}$$

The velocity is now:

$$\mathbf{v} = v\hat{\mathbf{s}} = \dot{s}\hat{\mathbf{s}}$$

The acceleration is obtained by differentiating with respect to t so that:

$$\mathbf{f} = \frac{d\mathbf{v}}{dt} = \frac{dv}{dt}\hat{\mathbf{s}} + v\frac{d\hat{\mathbf{s}}}{dt}$$

$$= \frac{dv}{dt}\hat{\mathbf{s}} + v\dot{\psi}\hat{\mathbf{n}}$$

Hence:

- the **acceleration** is the sum of two components:
  (i) $\dot{v}$ in the direction of the tangent (the **tangential component**)
  (ii) $v\dot{\psi}$ in the direction of the positive normal $\hat{\mathbf{n}}$ (the **normal component**).

Since:

$$v\dot{\psi} = v\frac{d\psi}{ds} \times \frac{ds}{dt} = v^2 \bigg/ \left(\frac{ds}{d\psi}\right)$$

the normal component can also be expressed in the form $\dfrac{v^2}{\rho}$ where ρ is the radius of curvature of the path at P.

- (ii)′ $\dfrac{v^2}{\rho}$ in the direction of the positive normal $\hat{\mathbf{n}}$ (the **normal component**)

The radius of curvature $\rho = \dfrac{ds}{d\psi}$ is positive if s increases as ψ increases, but is negative if s decreases as ψ increases.

The figures (a) to (d) illustrate four possible situations:

(a) Here $\dfrac{ds}{d\psi} = \rho > 0$

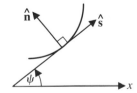

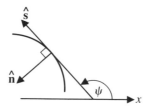

(b) Here $\dfrac{ds}{d\psi} = \rho > 0$

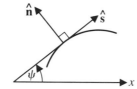

(c) Here $\dfrac{ds}{d\psi} = \rho < 0$

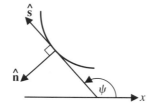

(d) Here $\dfrac{ds}{d\psi} = \rho < 0$

Therefore in (a) and (b), since $\dfrac{v^2}{\rho}$ is positive, the normal acceleration has the same sense as the positive normal.

However in (c) and (d), since $\dfrac{v^2}{\rho}$ is negative, the actual sense of the normal acceleration is opposite to that of the positive normal.

From the diagrams it is clear that in all cases the normal acceleration is directed to the concave side of the curve, that is, along the 'inward normal'.

The above results can therefore be written as follows:

- **The acceleration is the sum of two components:**
  (i) $\dot{v}$ in the direction of the tangent
  (ii) $\dfrac{v^2}{|\rho|}$ in the direction of the 'inward normal'.

Example 6

A particle P moves on the curve with equation $s = c \tan \psi$, where c is a constant. (This is the intrinsic equation of a catenary.) It moves with constant speed u. Obtain the normal and tangential components of P at the point where $\psi = \dfrac{\pi}{4}$.

When $\psi = \dfrac{\pi}{4}$ then $s = c$.

Since the speed is constant and equal to u the tangential component of the acceleration is zero.

For this curve $\rho = \dfrac{\mathrm{d}s}{\mathrm{d}\psi} = c \sec^2 \psi$ which is positive.

When $\psi = \dfrac{\pi}{4}$ then $\rho = c(\sqrt{2})^2 = 2c$.

Hence the normal component of acceleration is $\dfrac{u^2}{2c}$.

Example 7

A particle P moves on a plane curve in such a way that its tangential and normal components of acceleration are always constant. Show that if neither component vanishes, then the particle describes a logarithmic spiral with intrinsic equation:

$$s = Ae^{k\psi}$$

where A and k are constants.

Since the intrinsic equation is required first rewrite the tangential component using:

$$\frac{\mathrm{d}v}{\mathrm{d}t} = \frac{\mathrm{d}v}{\mathrm{d}s} \times \frac{\mathrm{d}s}{\mathrm{d}t} = v\frac{\mathrm{d}v}{\mathrm{d}s} = \frac{\mathrm{d}}{\mathrm{d}s}\left(\tfrac{1}{2}v^2\right)$$

Since this is constant:

$$\frac{\mathrm{d}}{\mathrm{d}s}\left(\tfrac{1}{2}v^2\right) = \alpha$$

Integration with respect to s gives:

$$\tfrac{1}{2}v^2 = \alpha s + \beta$$

Taking s to be zero when $v = 0$ gives $\beta = 0$ and so:

$$v^2 = 2\alpha s \qquad\qquad (1)$$

As the normal component is also constant:

$$\frac{v^2}{\rho} = v^2\frac{\mathrm{d}\psi}{\mathrm{d}s} = c$$

or: $$\frac{\mathrm{d}\psi}{\mathrm{d}s} = \frac{c}{v^2} \qquad\qquad (2)$$

Using equations (1) in (2) gives:

$$\frac{\mathrm{d}\psi}{\mathrm{d}s} = \frac{c}{2\alpha s}$$

Hence:
$$\frac{2\alpha}{c}\int \mathrm{d}\psi = \int \frac{\mathrm{d}s}{s}$$

Integrating:
$$\frac{2\alpha\psi}{c} = \ln s + \gamma$$

So:
$$s = \mathrm{e}^{\frac{2\alpha}{c}\psi - \gamma}$$

or:
$$s = A\mathrm{e}^{k\psi}$$

where $A = \mathrm{e}^{-\gamma}$ and $k = \dfrac{2\alpha}{c}$ are constants.

Example 8

A particle P moves along a curve whose equation is $s = \mathrm{f}(\psi)$ in such a way that the tangent rotates uniformly. Show that the normal acceleration is proportional to the radius of curvature at that point.

It is given that $\dfrac{\mathrm{d}\psi}{\mathrm{d}t} = k$.

Hence:
$$\rho = \frac{\mathrm{d}s}{\mathrm{d}\psi} = \frac{\dfrac{\mathrm{d}s}{\mathrm{d}t}}{\dfrac{\mathrm{d}\psi}{\mathrm{d}t}} = \frac{v}{k}$$

so:
$$v = k\rho$$

The normal component of acceleration is then:
$$\frac{v^2}{\rho} = \frac{k^2\rho^2}{\rho} = k^2\rho$$

and so the normal component of acceleration is proportional to ρ.

Example 9

A particle P moves along the curve with equation $y = x^3$, where x and y are in metres, with a constant speed of $10\,\mathrm{m\,s^{-1}}$. Find the acceleration of P at the point with coordinates $\left(\frac{1}{2}, \frac{1}{8}\right)$.

As P is moving with constant speed the tangential component of the acceleration is zero. It therefore suggests that intrinsic coordinates should be used.

In order to find the normal component of the acceleration we require ρ for this curve.

The formula for the radius of curvature, when the cartesian equation of the curve is given, can be found in Book P4 chapter 1. As you may not be taking Module P4, the derivation is repeated here.

Since the tangent to the curve makes an angle ψ with the x-axis:

$$\tan\psi = \frac{\mathrm{d}y}{\mathrm{d}x}$$

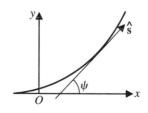

Differentiation of this equation with respect to s gives:

$$\sec^2\psi \, \frac{d\psi}{ds} = \frac{d^2y}{dx^2}\frac{dx}{ds}$$

From the diagram: $\dfrac{dx}{ds} = \cos\psi$

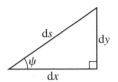

So: $\sec^2\psi \, \dfrac{d\psi}{ds} = \dfrac{d^2y}{dx^2}\cos\psi$

or: $\dfrac{d\psi}{ds} = \dfrac{d^2y}{dx^2} \times \dfrac{1}{\sec^3\psi}$

But $\sec^2\psi = 1 + \tan^2\psi = 1 + \left(\dfrac{dy}{dx}\right)^2$

Hence: $\dfrac{d\psi}{ds} = \dfrac{\dfrac{d^2y}{dx^2}}{\left[1 + \left(\dfrac{dy}{dx}\right)^2\right]^{\frac{3}{2}}}$

and: $\rho = \dfrac{ds}{d\psi} = \dfrac{\left[1 + \left(\dfrac{dy}{dx}\right)^2\right]^{\frac{3}{2}}}{\dfrac{d^2y}{dx^2}}$

So to obtain ρ for the given curve, $y = x^3$, we require:

$$\frac{dy}{dx} = 3x^2$$

and: $\dfrac{d^2y}{dx^2} = 6x$

At the point $\left(\tfrac{1}{2}, \tfrac{1}{8}\right)$:

$$\frac{dy}{dx} = 3\left(\tfrac{1}{4}\right) = \tfrac{3}{4}$$

and: $\dfrac{d^2y}{dx^2} = 6\left(\tfrac{1}{2}\right) = 3$

so: $\rho = \dfrac{\left[1 + \left(\tfrac{3}{4}\right)^2\right]^{\frac{3}{2}}}{3} = \dfrac{\left[1 + \tfrac{9}{16}\right]^{\frac{3}{2}}}{3} = \dfrac{\left[\tfrac{25}{16}\right]^{\frac{3}{2}}}{3} = \dfrac{125}{64 \times 3}$

The normal component of the acceleration is then:

$$\frac{v^2}{\rho} = (10)^2 \times \frac{64 \times 3}{125} = \frac{100}{125} \times 192$$

$$= 153.6\,\text{m s}^{-2}$$

Exercise 2A

1 A particle P moves in a plane so that its acceleration is $(-x\mathbf{i} - 4y\mathbf{j})\,\text{m s}^{-1}$ when its position vector is $(x\mathbf{i} + y\mathbf{j})\,\text{m}$. At time $t = 0$, the position vector of the particle is $(\mathbf{i} + \mathbf{j})\,\text{m}$ and its velocity is $(\mathbf{i} - 2\mathbf{j})\,\text{m s}^{-1}$. Find the position vector of P at time t.

2 A particle P moves in the plane of the rectangular axes Ox, Oy so that its acceleration is $-g\mathbf{j}$. When $t = 0$, $x = 0$ and $y = 0$ and its velocity is $(v\mathbf{i} + u\mathbf{j})$. Find the position vector of P at time t and the cartesian equation of the path of P.

3 A particle P moves in the plane of the rectangular axes Ox, Oy so that its acceleration at time t is:

$$(\omega^2 a \sin \omega t\,\mathbf{i} + \omega^2 a \cos \omega t\,\mathbf{j})$$

where a and ω are positive constants. It is projected at $t = 0$ with velocity $-\omega a\mathbf{i}$ from the point with position vector $-a\mathbf{j}$.
(a) Obtain the position vector of P at time t.
(b) Hence obtain the cartesian equation of the path of P.

4 The components of the velocity of a particle P along and perpendicular to the radius vector from a fixed origin O are λr^2 and $\mu\theta^2$ where λ and μ are positive constants. Find
(a) the polar equation of the path of the particle, and
(b) the radial and transverse components of the acceleration in terms of r and θ.

5 A particle P describes the equiangular spiral with polar equation $r = ae^{\theta}$ in such a way that its acceleration has no radial component. Show that
(a) the speed of the particle is proportional to r,
(b) the magnitude of the acceleration is proportional to r.

6 A particle P describes the curve with polar equation $r = a(1 + \cos \theta)$ in such a way that the radius vector from the origin (pole) rotates with uniform angular speed ω. Obtain the radial and transverse components of the velocity and acceleration of P at any time t, in terms of ω and θ.

7 A particle P moves in a plane. At time t seconds its polar coordinates (r, θ) relative to a fixed origin O are given by:

$$r = a(t^2 + t), \quad \theta = \tfrac{1}{6}t^3$$

where a is a positive constant. Find the speed of P when $t = 2$.

8 A particle P moves round the circle whose polar equation is $r = 2a \cos \theta,\ \dfrac{-\pi}{2} \leqslant \theta \leqslant \dfrac{\pi}{2}$, where a is a positive constant. It moves in such a way that its acceleration has no transverse component.

(a) Show that $\dot{r}$ is proportional to $\dfrac{\sin \theta}{r^2}$.

(b) Show that the radial acceleration is proportional to r^{-5}.

In questions 9, 10 and 11 you may assume that:

$$\rho = \frac{\left[1 + \left(\dfrac{\mathrm{d}y}{\mathrm{d}x}\right)^2\right]^{\frac{3}{2}}}{\dfrac{\mathrm{d}^2 y}{\mathrm{d}x^2}}.$$

9 A particle P moves on the curve with equation:

$$y = 1 - \frac{x^2}{4}$$

where x and y are in metres, with a constant speed of $12\,\mathrm{m\,s^{-1}}$. Find the acceleration of P at the point with coordinates $(0, 1)$

10 A particle P moves on the curve with equation:

$$y = \ln(\sec x)$$

in such a way that the tangent rotates uniformly. Show that the magnitude of the acceleration of P varies as ρ^2, where ρ is the radius of curvature.

11 A particle P moves on the curve with equation $y^2 = 4ax$ with a constant speed v. Show that the acceleration of P at the origin is of magnitude $\dfrac{v^2}{2a}$.

SUMMARY OF KEY POINTS

1 When cartesian coordinates (x, y) are used:

   velocity $\qquad\qquad \mathbf{v} = \dot{x}\mathbf{i} + \dot{y}\mathbf{j}$

   acceleration $\qquad\quad \mathbf{f} = \ddot{x}\mathbf{i} + \ddot{y}\mathbf{j}$

2 When polar coordinates (r, θ) are used:

   velocity $\qquad\qquad \mathbf{v} = \dot{r}\mathbf{e}_r + r\dot{\theta}\mathbf{e}_\theta$

   acceleration $\qquad\quad \mathbf{f} = \left(\ddot{r} - r\dot{\theta}^2\right)\mathbf{e}_r + \left(2\dot{r}\dot{\theta} + r\ddot{\theta}\right)\mathbf{e}_\theta$

$$= \left(\ddot{r} - r\dot{\theta}^2\right)\mathbf{e}_r + \frac{1}{r}\frac{\mathrm{d}}{\mathrm{d}t}\left(r^2\dot{\theta}\right)\mathbf{e}_\theta$$

   $\qquad\qquad\qquad$ (radial) $\qquad$ (transverse)

3 When intrinsic coordinates (s, ψ) are used:

   velocity $\qquad\qquad \mathbf{v} = \dot{s}\hat{\mathbf{s}}$

   acceleration $\qquad\quad \mathbf{f} = \ddot{s}\hat{\mathbf{s}} + \dfrac{v^2}{\rho}\hat{\mathbf{n}}$

   $\qquad\qquad$ (tangential) $\quad$ (normal)

   where ρ is the radius of curvature.

Dynamics of a particle moving in two dimensions

3

3.1 Motion of a particle on a curve

Consider a particle P, of mass m, moving with speed v on a plane. curve whose intrinsic equation is $s = f(\psi)$, where s is the arc length from a fixed point A on the curve to P, and ψ is the angle between the tangent at P and the x-axis.

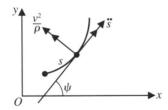

It was shown in chapter 2 that the acceleration of P is the sum of two components:

(i) $\ddot{s} = \dot{v}$ in the direction of the tangent

(ii) $\dfrac{v^2}{\rho} = \dfrac{\dot{s}^2}{\rho}$, where ρ is the radius of curvature, in the direction of the positive normal.

If the applied force $\mathbf{F}$ has components S and N tangential and normal to the curve then:

$$\mathbf{F} = S\hat{\mathbf{s}} + N\hat{\mathbf{n}}$$

■ **The tangential equation of motion is:**

$$m\dot{v} = S$$

and the normal equation of motion is:

$$\frac{mv^2}{\rho} = N$$

Motion of a particle on a smooth vertical curve

If the curve is smooth and fixed in a vertical plane, with Ox horizontal, then the forces acting on P are as shown in the diagram.

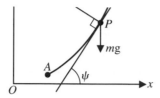

The tangential equation of motion is:

$$m\ddot{s} = -mg \sin \psi$$

and the normal equation of motion is:

$$R - mg \cos \psi = \frac{mv^2}{\rho}$$

Since $\ddot{s} = v\dfrac{\mathrm{d}v}{\mathrm{d}s}$ and $\sin \psi = \dfrac{\mathrm{d}y}{\mathrm{d}s}$, the tangential equation of motion may be written as:

$$mv\frac{\mathrm{d}v}{\mathrm{d}s} = -mg\frac{\mathrm{d}y}{\mathrm{d}s}$$

Integration with respect to s gives:

$$\tfrac{1}{2}mv^2 + mgy = k$$

where k is a constant. This is the **equation of energy**. It is often simpler when solving problems to use the energy equation rather than the equation of motion along the tangent.

Example 1

A smooth wire is bent into the form of an arch of a cycloid with intrinsic equation:

$$s = 4a \sin \psi, \quad -\frac{\pi}{2} \leqslant \psi \leqslant \frac{\pi}{2}$$

where a is a positive constant. The wire is fixed in a vertical plane with its axis vertical and its vertex O at its lowest point. A bead P, of mass m, moves under gravity on this wire starting from rest at the point Q where $\psi = \dfrac{\pi}{4}$.

(a) Obtain the time taken by P to move from Q to O.
(b) Obtain the normal contact force exerted on the bead by the wire when the bead is at O.

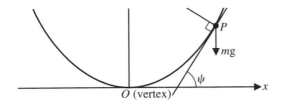

The diagram shows the forces acting on the bead P when the tangent to the curve makes an angle ψ with Ox, which is horizontal.

(a) The tangential equation of motion is:

$$m\ddot{s} = -mg \sin \psi \qquad (1)$$

But $s = 4a \sin \psi$ and so $\sin \psi = \dfrac{s}{4a}$ and:

$$\ddot{s} = -\frac{g}{4a} s \qquad (2)$$

This is of the form $\ddot{s} + \omega^2 s = 0$, with $\omega^2 = \dfrac{g}{4a}$.

It is the equation for simple harmonic motion (S.H.M.) of period $2\pi/\omega = 4\pi \sqrt{\left(\dfrac{a}{g}\right)}$ (see Book M2 chapter 2).

The general solution of the equation for S.H.M. is:

$$s = A \cos \omega t + B \sin \omega t$$

(see Book P2 chapter 8).

When $t = 0$, $\psi = \dfrac{\pi}{4}$ and $v = \dot{s} = 0$ as the bead starts from rest.

So $s = 2a\sqrt{2}$, $\dot{s} = 0$ when $t = 0$.

Hence $A = 2a\sqrt{2}$, $B = 0$ and:

$$s = 2a\sqrt{2} \cos \omega t$$

At O, the arc length $s = 0$ and so $\cos \omega t = 0$

$$\Rightarrow \qquad \omega t = \frac{\pi}{2}$$

$$t = \frac{\pi}{2\omega} = \pi \sqrt{\left(\frac{a}{g}\right)}$$

which is one quarter of the period.

The particle moves from Q to O in time $\pi \sqrt{\left(\dfrac{a}{g}\right)}$.

It is an important property of motion on a cycloid that the motion is always S.H.M. whatever its amplitude. Hence the period of oscillation is always the same, independent of the amplitude.

(b) The normal equation of motion is:

$$R - mg \cos \psi = \frac{mv^2}{\rho}$$

Instead of using equation (1), the tangential equation of motion, use the equation of energy.

This gives

$$\tfrac{1}{2}mv^2 + mgy_p = 0 + mgy_Q$$

or:

$$v^2 = 2g(y_Q - y_P)$$

Since $\dfrac{dy}{ds} = \sin \psi$, then:

$$\int dy = \int \sin \psi \, ds = \int \sin \psi \, \frac{ds}{d\psi} \, d\psi$$

$$= \int \sin \psi (4a \cos \psi) d\psi \quad \text{(using the equation of the curve).}$$

Hence: $y = 4a \times \tfrac{1}{2} \sin^2 \psi + K = 2a \sin^2 \psi + K$

where K is a constant.

So: $y_Q = 2a \times \tfrac{1}{2} + K \qquad \left(\psi = \dfrac{\pi}{4} \right)$

$$= a + K$$

$$y_P = 2a \sin^2 \psi + K$$

and: $y_Q - y_P = a(1 - 2 \sin^2 \psi) = a \cos 2\psi$

Hence: $v^2 = 2ag \cos 2\psi \hspace{2cm} (3)$

Also, since $s = 4a \sin \psi$,

$$\rho = \frac{ds}{d\psi} = 4a \cos \psi \hspace{2cm} (4)$$

Substituting from equations (3) and (4) into the equation of motion gives:

$$R = mg \cos \psi + \frac{2mag \cos 2\psi}{4a \cos \psi}$$

$$= mg \frac{(4 \cos^2 \psi - 1)}{2 \cos \psi}$$

Notice that for $0 \leqslant \psi \leqslant \dfrac{\pi}{4}$, $4\cos^2\psi - 1 > 0$ and therefore R is positive throughout the motion from Q to O. At O, $\psi = 0$ and $R = \dfrac{3mg}{2}$.

Example 2

A smooth wire in the form of an arch of the cycloid, with intrinsic equation $s = 4a \sin \psi$, is fixed in a vertical plane with its vertex downwards. The tangent at the vertex is horizontal. A small bead, of mass m, is threaded on the wire and is subject to an air resistance of magnitude $\dfrac{mv^2}{8a}$ when its speed is v.

Given that the bead is projected from the vertex with speed $\sqrt{(8ga)}$, show that the bead comes to instantaneous rest at a cusp where $s = 4a$.

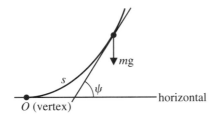

Suppose that, after a time t, the bead is moving away from the vertex O with speed v having moved a distance s along the cycloid.

The equation of motion of the bead along the tangent is:

$$mv\frac{\mathrm{d}v}{\mathrm{d}s} = -mg \sin \psi - \frac{mv^2}{8a} \qquad (1)$$

Since v^2 occurs on the right-hand side, write:

$$v\frac{dv}{ds} = \frac{\mathrm{d}}{\mathrm{d}s}\left(\tfrac{1}{2}v^2\right)$$

Using this result and the equation of the curve in (1) gives:

$$\frac{\mathrm{d}(v^2)}{\mathrm{d}s} + \frac{v^2}{4a} = -\frac{gs}{2a} \qquad (2)$$

This is a linear differential equation of the first order for v^2 (see Book P3 chapter 8). It may be solved by means of the integrating factor $e^{\frac{s}{4a}}$.

Multiplying equation (2) by this factor gives:

$$\frac{\mathrm{d}}{\mathrm{d}s}\left[v^2 e^{\frac{s}{4a}}\right] = -\frac{gs}{2a}e^{\frac{s}{4a}}$$

Integrating:

$$v^2 e^{\frac{s}{4a}} = -\frac{g}{2a} \int s e^{\frac{s}{4a}} \, ds$$

$$= -g\left[2s e^{\frac{s}{4a}} - 8a e^{\frac{s}{4a}}\right] + c$$

using integration by parts.

So:

$$v^2 = c e^{-\frac{s}{4a}} - 2gs + 8ga$$

As $v^2 = 8ga$ when $s = 0$, then:

$$8ga = c + 8ga$$

so:

$$c = 0$$

and:

$$v^2 = 2g(4a - s)$$

The bead will therefore come instantaneously to rest when $s = 4a$, that is, when $\psi = \dfrac{\pi}{2}$ and the bead is at a cusp.

Example 3

The cross-section of a smooth surface has the equation:

$$y = a\left[\cosh\left(\frac{x}{a}\right) - 1\right]$$

where the x-axis is horizontal and the y-axis is vertically downwards as shown in the diagram.

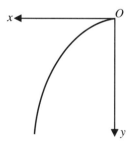

A particle of mass m is projected from O with a horizontal speed of u.

(a) Show that if $u^2 > ga$ the particle will leave the surface immediately.

(b) Show that if $u^2 < ga$ the particle will leave the surface when

$$y = a - \frac{u^2}{g}$$

The forces acting on the particle when it is at the point (x, y) on the curve are shown in the diagram.

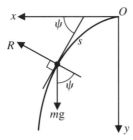

Notice that in this situation the angle ψ is acute and the radius of curvature positive, so that the positive normal coincides with the inward normal. If a choice is available you should always choose your axes so that this happens.

At any point on the curve:

$$\tan \psi = \frac{\mathrm{d}y}{\mathrm{d}x} = \sinh\left(\frac{x}{a}\right)$$

and so:

$$\rho = \frac{\left[1 + \left(\dfrac{\mathrm{d}y}{\mathrm{d}x}\right)^2\right]^{\frac{3}{2}}}{\dfrac{\mathrm{d}^2 y}{\mathrm{d}x^2}}$$

$$= \frac{\left[1 + \sinh^2\left(\dfrac{x}{a}\right)\right]^{\frac{3}{2}}}{\dfrac{1}{a}\cosh\dfrac{x}{a}} = \frac{\cosh^3\left(\dfrac{x}{a}\right)}{\dfrac{1}{a}\cosh\left(\dfrac{x}{a}\right)}$$

$$= a \cosh^2\left(\frac{x}{a}\right)$$

While the particle is still on the curve we may use the equation of energy to find the speed v. If the particle is at (x, y) then:

$$\tfrac{1}{2}mv^2 - mgy = \tfrac{1}{2}mu^2$$

so that:

$$v^2 = u^2 + 2gy \qquad (1)$$

The equation of motion along the inward normal is:

$$\frac{mv^2}{\rho} = mg \cos \psi - R \qquad (2)$$

But: $\quad \cos \psi = \dfrac{1}{\sec \psi} = \dfrac{1}{\sqrt{(1 + \tan^2\psi)}} = \dfrac{1}{\sqrt{\left(1 + \sinh^2\left(\dfrac{x}{a}\right)\right)}}$

$$= \frac{1}{\cosh\left(\dfrac{x}{a}\right)} \qquad (3)$$

Using (1) and (3) in equation (2) gives:

$$R = \frac{mg}{\cosh\left(\dfrac{x}{a}\right)} - \frac{m(u^2 + 2gy)}{a \cosh^2\left(\dfrac{x}{a}\right)}$$

$$= \frac{mg\, a \cosh\dfrac{x}{a} - m(u^2 + 2gy)}{a \cosh^2\left(\dfrac{x}{a}\right)}$$

and using the equation of the curve:

$$R = \frac{mg(y + a) - m(u^2 + 2gy)}{a \cosh^2\left(\dfrac{x}{a}\right)}$$

$$= \frac{m(ga - u^2) - mgy}{a \cosh^2\left(\dfrac{x}{a}\right)} \tag{4}$$

(a) If $u^2 > ga$ then R, given by equation (4), is negative for all positive values of y. Hence the particle leaves the surface immediately.

(b) If $u^2 < ga$ the value of R is initially positive but becomes zero when

$$m(ga - u^2) = mgy$$

so:

$$y = a - \frac{u^2}{g}$$

Hence the particle leaves the surface when it has descended this distance.

Exercise 3A

1 A smooth wire is bent into the form of an arch of a cycloid with intrinsic equation:

$$s = 4a \sin \psi, \quad -\frac{\pi}{2} \leqslant \psi \leqslant \frac{\pi}{2}$$

where a is a positive constant. The wire is fixed in a vertical plane with its axis vertical and its vertex O at its lowest point. A bead P, of mass m, moves under gravity on this wire. Given that the bead is projected from the vertex O with speed $2\sqrt{(ga)}$, show that when P reaches the point at which the tangent is inclined at an angle θ to the horizontal:

(a) its speed is $2\sqrt{(ga)}\cos\theta$

(b) the normal contact force exerted by the wire on the bead is $2\,mg\cos\theta$.

2 A smooth wire in the form of an arch of a cycloid with intrinsic equation:

$$s = 4a\sin\psi,\ -\frac{\pi}{2} \leqslant \psi \leqslant \frac{\pi}{2}$$

is fixed in a vertical plane, the vertex O being the lowest point of the wire where the tangent is horizontal. A bead, of mass m, which can slide freely on the wire is released from rest at the point where $\psi = \frac{\pi}{6}$.

(a) Find the periodic time of oscillation of the bead.

(b) Show that the normal contact force exerted by the wire on the bead at a point where the tangent makes an angle θ with the horizontal is:

$$\tfrac{1}{4}\,mg\sec\theta\,(8\cos^2\theta - 3)$$

3 A particle P of unit mass slides down a tube in the form of a cycloid $s = 4a\sin\psi$ with its axis vertical and vertex downwards. The particle starts from rest at a cusp $\left(\psi = \dfrac{\pi}{2}\right)$. The resistance to motion along the tube is kv^2 where v is the speed of P. Find the speed v_0 of P at the vertex and show that when k is small

$$v_0 = \left(1 - \tfrac{8}{3}ak\right)u$$

where u is the speed at the vertex when k is zero.

4 A smooth wire is bent into the form of the curve c with equation:

$$y = \ln\sec x,\ 0 \leqslant x < \frac{\pi}{2}$$

The wire is fixed in a vertical plane with the y-axis vertically downwards and a small bead of mass m is placed at the origin. The bead is displaced gently from rest.

(a) Show that the magnitude of the normal contact force exerted by the wire on the bead at the point where $x = \dfrac{\pi}{3}$ is:

$$mg\left(\ln 2 - \tfrac{1}{2}\right)$$

(b) Show further that when the normal contact force vanishes instantaneously, the tangential acceleration of the bead is:

$$g\sqrt{\left(\frac{e-1}{e}\right)}$$

5 A particle P slides down a smooth curve, fixed in a vertical plane, which is bent into the form of the catenary:

$$y = a\cosh\left(\frac{x}{a}\right)$$

the y-axis being vertically upwards. The particle is given a speed along the curve, when at its highest point, of magnitude $\sqrt{\left(\dfrac{ga}{2}\right)}$.

(a) Show that, when P is moving on the curve in a direction making an angle ψ to the horizontal, its speed v is given by:

$$v^2 = \tfrac{1}{2}\,ga(4\sec\psi - 3)$$

(b) Show that the particle leaves the curve when $\cos\psi = \tfrac{2}{3}$.

6 A small bead P, of mass m, moves on a smooth wire, which is bent into the form with equation:

$$y = \cos x \qquad (0 \leqslant x \leqslant \pi)$$

The wire is fixed in a vertical plane with the y-axis vertical. The bead is just disturbed from the point with coordinates $(0, 1)$.

(a) Calculate the speed of P at the point $\left(\dfrac{\pi}{2}, 0\right)$.

(b) Calculate the magnitude of the normal contact force exerted by the wire on the bead when P is at $\left(\dfrac{\pi}{2}, 0\right)$.

3.2 Motion of a particle under a central force

Consider now a particle moving in a plane under the action of a force which is always directed towards or away from a fixed point O in the plane. Such a force is called a **central force**. The path described by the particle is called a **central orbit** and the fixed point O is called the **centre of force**.

If the point O is taken as the pole of a system of polar coordinates, then the force is always along the radial direction. In problems of this kind it is therefore appropriate to use the components of acceleration in the radial and transverse directions. These were obtained in chapter 2.

Consider a particle P, of mass m, which is subject to a force of magnitude f(r) along PO, where the distance OP is r. This is an attractive central force.

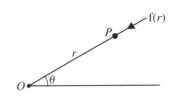

■ **The radial equation of motion is:**

$$m\left(\ddot{r} - r\,\dot{\theta}^2\right) = -\mathbf{f}(r) \qquad (1)$$

and the transverse equation of motion is:

$$m\left(2\dot{r}\,\dot{\theta} + r\ddot{\theta}\right) = 0$$

or:

$$\frac{m}{r}\frac{d}{dt}\left(r^2\dot{\theta}\right) = 0 \qquad (2)$$

Equation (2) may be integrated to give:

$$r^2\dot{\theta} = h \qquad (3)$$

where h is a constant.

It was shown in chapter 2 that the velocity of P is:

$$\mathbf{v} = \dot{r}\mathbf{e}_r + r\dot{\theta}\mathbf{e}_\theta$$

and so the momentum of P is:

$$m\mathbf{v} = m\dot{r}\mathbf{e}_r + mr\dot{\theta}\mathbf{e}_\theta$$

The moment of this momentum about O is:

$$\mathbf{r} \times m\mathbf{v} = r\mathbf{e}_r \times \left(m\dot{r}\mathbf{e}_r + mr\dot{\theta}\mathbf{e}_\theta\right)$$

Since $\mathbf{e}_r \times \mathbf{e}_r = \mathbf{0}$ then:

$$\mathbf{r} \times m\mathbf{v} = mr^2\dot{\theta}\,\mathbf{k}$$

where $\mathbf{k} = \mathbf{e}_r \times \mathbf{e}_\theta$ is a unit vector perpendicular to the plane of motion.

Using $r^2\dot{\theta} = h$ we see that the moment of the momentum about O has a constant magnitude mh.

■ **When a particle moves under a central force its moment of momentum about the centre of force remains constant.**

Suppose the particle P has speed v. This speed is of course along the tangent to the path. If the length of ON, the perpendicular from O to this tangent, is p then the moment of the momentum about O has magnitude mpv.

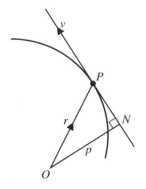

Comparing this with equation (3):

$$r^2\dot\theta = h = pv.$$

The value of h may be obtained using any convenient point on the path.

Elimination of $\dot\theta$ between equations (1) and (3) will produce an equation involving only r and its derivatives.

Equation (3) may be rewritten as $\dot\theta = \dfrac{h}{r^2}$

So equation (1) becomes:

$$\ddot{r} - r\left(\frac{h^2}{r^4}\right) = -\frac{f(r)}{m}$$

or:
$$\ddot{r} = \frac{h^2}{r^3} - \frac{f(r)}{m} \tag{4}$$

Given a specific form for $f(r)$, the integration of this equation can now be attempted.

However for general $f(r)$, the form of the energy equation for a central orbit can be obtained.

Multiplying equation (4) by $\dot{r}$ gives:

$$\dot{r}\ddot{r} = \frac{h^2\dot{r}}{r^3} - \frac{f(r)\dot{r}}{m}$$

Integration with respect to t gives:

$$\tfrac{1}{2}\dot{r}^2 = -\frac{h^2}{2r^2} - \frac{1}{m}\int f(r)\mathrm{d}r + c$$

where c is a constant.

Using $h = r^2\dot\theta$ this may be written:

■
$$\tfrac{1}{2}m\left(\dot{r}^2 + r^2\dot\theta^2\right) + \int f(r)\mathrm{d}r = \text{constant}$$

The first term is just $\tfrac{1}{2}mv^2$ and so this is the energy equation for a central orbit.

Example 4

A particle P, of mass m, is attached to one end of a light elastic spring of natural length a and modulus $2mg$. The other end of the spring is attached to a fixed point O on a smooth horizontal table on which P is free to move.

The particle is projected horizontally with speed $3\sqrt{(ga)}$ in a direction perpendicular to the spring with the spring at its natural length.

(a) Show that when the length of the spring is r, in the subsequent motion, its angular speed is $\dfrac{3}{r^2}\sqrt{(ga^3)}$.

(b) Show that the radial speed of the particle is zero when $r = 3a$ and deduce that r satisfies the inequality $a \leqslant r \leqslant 3a$.

The only force acting on P is the tension T in the string which acts towards O and is of magnitude:

$$T = \frac{2mg(r-a)}{a}$$

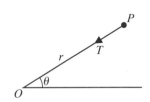

when $OP = r$.

(a) Since the force is central, the transverse equation of motion is:

$$\frac{1}{r}\frac{\mathrm{d}}{\mathrm{d}t}\left(r^2\dot{\theta}\right) = 0$$

and so $\qquad r^2\dot{\theta} = h \qquad$ (constant).

The initial conditions are shown in the diagram.

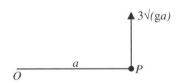

Hence: $\qquad h = pv$

$$= a(3\sqrt{ga}) = 3\sqrt{(ga^3)}$$

so: $\qquad r^2\dot{\theta} = 3\sqrt{(ga^3)}$

and: $\qquad \dot{\theta} = \dfrac{3}{r^2}\sqrt{(ga^3)}$

(b) The radial equation of motion is:

$$m\left(\ddot{r} - r\dot{\theta}^2\right) = -T = -\frac{2mg}{a}(r-a)$$

Substituting for $\dot{\theta}$ gives:

$$\ddot{r} - r\left(\frac{9ga^3}{r^4}\right) = -\frac{2g}{a}(r-a)$$

Multiplying by $\dot{r}$ gives:

$$\ddot{r}\dot{r} - \frac{9ga^3}{r^3}\dot{r} = -\frac{2g}{a}(r-a)\dot{r}$$

Integrating with respect to t:

$$\tfrac{1}{2}\dot{r}^2 + \frac{9ga^3}{2r^2} = -\frac{\cancel{2}g}{a}\frac{(r-a)^2}{\cancel{2}} + C$$

where C is a constant.

Using $\dot{r} = 0$ when $r = a$, (the particle is projected perpendicular to the spring), gives:

$$C = \frac{9ga^3}{2a^2} = \tfrac{9}{2}ga$$

so:
$$\tfrac{1}{2}\dot{r}^2 = -\frac{g}{a}(r - a)^2 + \tfrac{9}{2}ga\left(1 - \frac{a^2}{r^2}\right)$$

$$= \frac{-2gr^2(r - a)^2 + 9ga^2(r^2 - a^2)}{2ar^2}$$

$$= \frac{g}{2ar^2}(r - a)[-2r^2(r - a) + 9a^2(r + a)]$$

$$= \frac{g}{2ar^2}(r - a)[-2r^3 + 2r^2a + 9a^2r + 9a^3]$$

$$= \frac{g}{2ar^2}(r - a)(3a - r)(3a^2 + 4ar + 2r^2)$$

Hence $\dot{r} = 0$ when $r = 3a$.

Consider the quadratic expression $2r^2 + 4ar + 3a^2$.

The equation:

$$2r^2 + 4ar + 3a^2 = 0$$

has no real roots. For $r = a$ the expression is obviously positive and so must be positive for all values of r.

So $\dot{r}^2 \geqslant 0$ if $(r - a)(3a - r) \geqslant 0$ and hence $a \leqslant r \leqslant 3a$.

Example 5
A particle P of mass m moves on the curve with polar equation:

$$\frac{a}{r} = 1 + e \cos \theta$$

where a and e are positive constants and $e < 1$, under the action of a force $mf(r)$ which is directed towards O. Show that:

(a) $r^2\dot{\theta} = h$, where h is a constant

(b) $\dot{r} = \dfrac{he}{a} \sin \theta$

(c) $f(r) = \dfrac{h^2}{ar^2}$

(d) if v is the speed of P when it is at a distance r from O then:

$$v^2 - \frac{2h^2}{ar} = \frac{h^2}{a^2}(e^2 - 1)$$

(a) As the force is a central force the transverse equation of motion gives

$$\frac{1}{r}\frac{d}{dt}\left(r^2\dot{\theta}\right) = 0$$

so:

$$r^2\dot{\theta} = h$$

where h is constant.

(b) From the given equation of the orbit, differentiating with respect to t gives:

$$-\frac{a}{r^2}\dot{r} = -e\sin\theta\,\dot{\theta}$$

so:

$$\dot{r} = \frac{er^2}{a}\sin\theta\,\dot{\theta}$$

But $r^2\dot{\theta} = h$ and therefore $\dot{r} = \frac{eh}{a}\sin\theta$.

(c) The radial equation of motion is:

$$m\left(\ddot{r} - r\dot{\theta}^2\right) = -m\mathrm{f}(r)$$

To obtain $\mathrm{f}(r)$ it is necessary to find $\ddot{r}$. Differentiating the result found in (b) for $\dot{r}$ gives:

$$\ddot{r} = \frac{eh}{a}\cos\theta\,\dot{\theta}$$

and using $\dot{\theta} = \frac{h}{r^2}$ we obtain:

$$\ddot{r} = \frac{eh}{a}\frac{h}{r^2}\cos\theta = \frac{eh^2}{ar^2}\cos\theta$$

Using $\mathrm{f}(r) = r\dot{\theta}^2 - \ddot{r}$ and substituting for $\dot{\theta}$ and $\ddot{r}$ gives:

$$\mathrm{f}(r) = r\left(\frac{h}{r^2}\right)^2 - \frac{eh^2}{ar^2}\cos\theta$$

$$= \frac{h^4}{r^3} - \frac{h^2}{ar^2}e\cos\theta$$

But $e\cos\theta = \frac{a}{r} - 1$ from the orbit equation and so:

$$\mathrm{f}(r) = \frac{h^4}{r^3} - \frac{h^2}{ar^2}\left(\frac{a}{r} - 1\right) = \frac{h^2}{ar^2}$$

Hence the law of force is the inverse square law of force, used in Book M2 chapter 2, when Newton's law of gravitation was considered. (The polar equation given in the question is that of an ellipse.)

(d) The components of velocity in polar coordinates are $\dot{r}$ and $r\dot{\theta}$, as shown in chapter 2.

Hence if v is the speed of P, then:

$$v^2 = \dot{r}^2 + r^2\dot{\theta}^2$$

Using $\dot{\theta} = \dfrac{h}{r^2}$ and $\dot{r} = \dfrac{eh}{a}\sin\theta$ gives:

$$v^2 = \frac{e^2 h^2}{a^2}\sin^2\theta + r^2\left(\frac{h}{r^2}\right)^2$$

$$= \frac{e^2 h^2}{a^2}(1 - \cos^2\theta) + \frac{h^2}{r^2}$$

But $e\cos\theta = \left(\dfrac{a}{r} - 1\right)$ from the equation of the orbit.

So:

$$v^2 = \frac{e^2 h^2}{a^2} - \frac{h^2}{a^2}\left(\frac{a}{r} - 1\right)^2 + \frac{h^2}{r^2}$$

$$= \frac{e^2 h^2}{a^2} - \frac{h^2}{a^2}\left(\frac{a^{\cancel{2}}}{\cancel{r^2}} - \frac{2a}{r} + 1\right) + \frac{h^{\cancel{2}}}{\cancel{r^2}}$$

or:

$$v^2 - \frac{2h^2}{ar} = \frac{h^2}{a^2}(e^2 - 1)$$

Since $e < 1$ this also shows that $v^2 - \dfrac{2h^2}{ar}$ is negative.

Example 6

A particle P, of mass m, lies on a smooth table and is attached, by a light inextensible string of length $2l$ passing through a small hole O in the table, to a particle Q, of mass m, hanging vertically. Initially OP is of length l and P is projected at right angles to OP with speed $\left(\dfrac{8gl}{3}\right)^{\frac{1}{2}}$. If r is the distance of P from the hole at time t, show that:

(a) $\dot{r}^2 = \dfrac{7gl}{3} - \dfrac{4gl^3}{3r^2} - gr$

(b) Q will just reach O

(c) the tension T in the string is given by:

$$T = \frac{mg}{2}\left(1 + \frac{8l^3}{3r^3}\right)$$

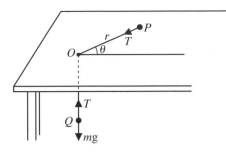

The only force acting on P is the tension T in the string. This acts along PO and so P is subject to a central force. Using polar coordinates (r, θ) on the table with O as the pole and some fixed line in the table as the initial line, we have as before:

$$r^2\dot{\theta} = h \text{ (constant)}$$

From the initial conditions when $t = 0$, $r = l$ and $r\dot{\theta} = \left(\dfrac{8gl}{3}\right)^{\frac{1}{2}}$ so

$$h = l\left(\frac{8gl}{3}\right)^{\frac{1}{2}} = \left(\frac{8gl^3}{3}\right)^{\frac{1}{2}}.$$

Since $OP = r$ the length of OQ is $2l - r$ and so the speed of Q is

$$\frac{\mathrm{d}}{\mathrm{d}t}(2l - r) = -\dot{r}.$$

The kinetic energy of P is $\frac{1}{2}m\left(\dot{r}^2 + r^2\dot{\theta}^2\right)$ and the kinetic energy of Q is $\frac{1}{2}m\dot{r}^2$.

The potential energy of Q is $-mg(2l - r)$.

Hence the energy equation gives:

$$\tfrac{1}{2}m\left(\dot{r}^2 + r^2\dot{\theta}^2\right) + \tfrac{1}{2}m\left(\dot{r}^2\right) - mg(2l - r) = C \text{ (constant)}$$

As $\dot{r} = 0$, $r = l$ and $r\dot{\theta} = \left(\dfrac{8gl}{3}\right)^{\frac{1}{2}}$ at $t = 0$:

$$C = \frac{mgl}{3}$$

So:

$$\dot{r}^2 + \tfrac{1}{2}r^2\dot{\theta}^2 - 2gl + gr = \frac{gl}{3}$$

or:

$$\dot{r}^2 + \tfrac{1}{2}r^2\dot{\theta}^2 + gr = \frac{7gl}{3}$$

But $\dot{\theta} = \dfrac{h}{r^2} = \left(\dfrac{8gl^3}{3}\right)^{\frac{1}{2}} \dfrac{1}{r^2}$

So:

$$\dot{r}^2 = \frac{7gl}{3} - gr - \frac{1}{2}\frac{r^2}{r^4}\frac{8gl^3}{3}$$

(a)
$$\dot{r}^2 = \frac{7gl}{3} - \frac{4gl}{3r^2} - gr$$

So $\dot{r} = 0$ when:

$$7lr^2 - 4l^3 - 3r^3 = 0$$

or:

$$3r^3 - 7lr^2 + 4l^3 = 0$$

It is known that $\dot{r} = 0$ when $r = l$ so $(r - l)$ must be a factor of the cubic. So:

$$(r - l)(3r^2 - 4lr - 4l^2) = 0$$

and:

$$(r - l)(3r + 2l)(r - 2l) = 0$$

so $r = l$ or $r = 2l$.

(b) When $r = 2l$ then $OQ = 0$ and Q just reaches the hole O.

The equation of motion of P radially is:

$$m\left(\ddot{r} - r\dot{\theta}^2\right) = -T$$

The equation of motion of Q vertically downwards is:

$$m\frac{d^2}{dt^2}(2l - r) = mg - T$$

or:

$$-m\ddot{r} = mg - T$$

Adding the two equations of motion gives:

$$-mr\dot{\theta}^2 = mg - 2T$$

So:

$$2T = m\left(g + r\dot{\theta}^2\right)$$

But $\dot{\theta}^2 = \dfrac{h^2}{r^4} = \dfrac{8gl^3}{3r^4}$

So:

$$T = \frac{mg}{2}\left(1 + \frac{8l^3}{3r^3}\right)$$

Example 7

A particle, of mass m, is projected from a point A, at a distance a from a fixed point O, with a velocity $\dfrac{\sqrt{\mu}}{a}$, in the direction AP where the angle OAP is $45°$. It is subject to a force $\dfrac{\mu m}{r^3}$ directed towards O, where r is the distance from O. Show that the orbit of the particle has the polar equation

$$r = ae^{-\theta}$$

The initial conditions of projection are summarised in the diagram.

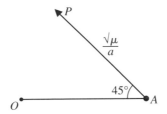

Hence when $t = 0$,

$$\dot{r} = -\frac{\sqrt{\mu}}{a} \cos 45° = -\frac{1}{a}\sqrt{\left(\frac{\mu}{2}\right)}$$

and:

$$r\dot{\theta} = \frac{\sqrt{\mu}}{a} \sin 45° = \frac{1}{a}\sqrt{\left(\frac{\mu}{2}\right)}.$$

As the motion is caused by a central force the transverse equation of motion is:

$$\frac{1}{r}\frac{\mathrm{d}}{\mathrm{d}t}\left(r^2\dot{\theta}\right) = 0$$

So $r^2\dot{\theta} = h$ (constant).

Using the initial conditions $r = a$, $r\dot{\theta} = \frac{1}{a}\sqrt{\left(\frac{\mu}{2}\right)}$ gives:

$$h = \sqrt{\left(\frac{\mu}{2}\right)}$$

The radial equation of motion is:

$$m\left(\ddot{r} - r\dot{\theta}^2\right) = -\frac{\mu m}{r^3}$$

Substituting $\dot{\theta} = \frac{h}{r^2}$ gives:

$$\ddot{r} - \frac{h^2}{r^3} = -\frac{\mu}{r^3}$$

$$\ddot{r} = \frac{(h^2 - \mu)}{r^3} = -\frac{\mu}{2r^3}$$

Multiplying by $\dot{r}$ and integrating with respect to t gives:

$$\tfrac{1}{2}\dot{r}^2 = \frac{\mu}{2 \times 2r^2} + C, \text{ where } C \text{ is a constant}$$

Using the initial conditions $\dot{r} = -\frac{1}{a}\sqrt{\left(\frac{\mu}{2}\right)}$ and $r = a$ gives:

$$C = \frac{1}{2}\frac{\mu}{2}\frac{1}{a^2} - \frac{\mu}{2 \times 2a^2} = 0$$

So:
$$\dot{r}^2 = \frac{\mu}{2r^2}$$

And:
$$\dot{r} = \pm\frac{1}{r}\sqrt{\left(\frac{\mu}{2}\right)}$$

Since $\dot{r} = -\frac{1}{a}\sqrt{\left(\frac{\mu}{2}\right)}$ initially then the negative sign is required so that:

$$\dot{r} = -\frac{1}{r}\sqrt{\left(\frac{\mu}{2}\right)}$$

Also we know that $\dot{\theta} = \frac{1}{r^2}\sqrt{\left(\frac{\mu}{2}\right)}$

Hence: $\dfrac{\mathrm{d}r}{\mathrm{d}\theta} = \dfrac{\dot{r}}{\dot{\theta}} = \dfrac{-\dfrac{1}{r}\sqrt{\left(\dfrac{\mu}{2}\right)}}{\dfrac{1}{r^2}\sqrt{\left(\dfrac{\mu}{2}\right)}} = -r$

Integrating:
$$\int\frac{\mathrm{d}r}{r} = -\int\mathrm{d}\theta$$

$$\ln r = -\theta + k$$

so that:
$$r = \mathrm{e}^{-\theta+k}$$

But when $\theta = 0$, initially $r = a$ so that $a = \mathrm{e}^k$

and:
$$r = a\mathrm{e}^{-\theta}$$

Exercise 3B

1 A particle P, of mass m, is held at rest on a smooth table. A light inextensible string is attached to this particle, passes through a hole O in the table and supports a particle Q of mass $3m$. Particle P is projected with speed v perpendicular to the string when P is at a distance a from O. Show that when Q has descended a distance $\frac{1}{2}a$ its speed will be:

$$\tfrac{1}{2}[3(ga - v^2)]^{\frac{1}{2}}$$

2 One end of an elastic string of modulus mg and natural length a is attached to a fixed point O on a smooth horizontal table and the other to a particle P of mass m on the table. The particle is

projected with speed v in a direction perpendicular to the string when the length of the string is $3a$. Given that the maximum length of the string in the subsequent motion is $5a$, show that:

$$v^2 = \tfrac{75}{4}\, ga$$

3 A particle moves round the circle with polar equation

$r = 2a \cos \theta, -\dfrac{\pi}{2} \leqslant \theta \leqslant \dfrac{\pi}{2}$, a a positive constant, under the action of a force of attraction directed towards O, the pole.

(a) Show that $\dot{r} = -\dfrac{2ah}{r^2} \sin \theta$, where $h = r^2 \dot{\theta}$.

(b) Show also that the magnitude of the force is proportional to r^{-5}.   [L]

4 At time t the polar coordinates of a particle of unit mass moving in a plane are (r, θ). The only force acting on the particle is

$$\mathbf{F} = \frac{\mu}{r^3}\, \mathbf{e}_r$$

where μ is constant and $\mathbf{e}_r$ is a unit vector along the radial direction. Show that

(a) $\dfrac{d\theta}{dt} = \dfrac{h}{r^2}$

(b) $\dfrac{d^2 r}{dt^2} = \dfrac{\mu + h^2}{r^3}$, where h is constant.

5 A particle P, of unit mass, moves on a smooth horizontal plane under the action of a force of magnitude $\left(w^2 r + \dfrac{w^2 a^3}{r^2} \right)$ directed towards a fixed point O of the plane; where w is a constant and $OP = r$.

The particle is projected from a point, a distance a from O, with a horizontal speed $\dfrac{4aw}{\sqrt{3}}$ in a direction perpendicular to OP.

(a) Show that in the subsequent motion

$$\dot{r}^2 = w^2 (r - a)(2a - r)(3r^2 + 9ar + 8a^2)/(3r^2)$$

(b) Deduce that r lies between a and $2a$.

6 A particle P moves in a path with polar equation

$$r = \frac{2a}{2 + \cos \theta}$$

with respect to a pole O and initial line OA. At any time t during the motion $r^2\dot{\theta} = h$ (constant). Show that the acceleration of P is directed towards O and that its magnitude is inversely proportional to r^2.

7 The only force acting on a body, which is of mass M and is at a distance r from the centre of the Earth, is directed towards the centre of the Earth and is of magnitude $\dfrac{\mu M}{r^2}$, where μ is a constant. Show that the speed of a satellite of mass m moving in a circular orbit of radius a about the centre of the Earth is $\sqrt{\left(\dfrac{\mu}{a}\right)}$.

A second satellite, of mass $3m$, is moving in the same circular orbit as the first but in the opposite direction and the two satellites collide and coalesce to form a single composite body. Show that the subsequent motion of the composite body is governed by the two equations:

$$r^2\dot{\theta} = \sqrt{\left(\frac{a\mu}{4}\right)}$$

$$\ddot{r} = \frac{\mu(a - 4r)}{4r^3}$$

where (r, θ) are the polar coordinates of the body with the centre of the Earth as pole.

Find the values of r when $\dot{r}^2 = 0$. [L]

3.3 Motion of projectiles

Chapter 3 of Book M1 dealt with some simple cases of the motion of a projectile. Considerations there were restricted to situations where the constant acceleration equations could be used in horizontal and vertical directions. In addition, the particle under consideration was implicitly assumed to be inelastic. Some more general aspects of projectile motion are considered in this chapter.

Motion of an elastic particle in a vertical plane

If a rubber ball is thrown into the air, then after describing the usual parabolic path it will strike the ground. In general it will then rebound and describe another smaller parabolic path. The following examples indicate how such situations can be dealt with.

The ball is modelled by an elastic particle. It is assumed that gravity is constant, that there is no air resistance and that motion takes place in a vertical plane.

Example 8

A boy throws a rubber ball with speed u at an angle θ to the horizontal so that it strikes a smooth vertical wall, perpendicular to its plane of motion, which is at a distance a from him. The ball returns to his hand. Given that e is the coefficient of restitution between the ball and the wall, show that

$$u^2 \sin 2\theta = \frac{ga}{e}(1 + e)$$

The vertical equation of motion is:

$$\ddot{y} = -g$$

Integrating this with respect to t and using the given initial condition that $\dot{y} = u \sin \theta$ at $t = 0$ gives:

$$\dot{y} = u \sin \theta - gt$$

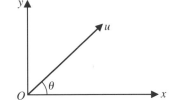

Assuming $y = 0$ at $t = 0$, a further integration with respect to t gives:

$$y = ut \sin \theta - \tfrac{1}{2} gt^2$$

When the ball strikes the wall the vertical component of the velocity is unchanged and so the time of flight is unchanged. This is obtained from $y = 0$. So the time of flight T is:

$$T = \frac{2u \sin \theta}{g}$$

The horizontal velocity of the ball before it strikes the wall is equal to its initial value $u \cos \theta$ and so the ball takes a time $\dfrac{a}{u \cos \theta}$ to reach the wall.

As seen in chapter 5 of Book M2, the ball rebounds from the wall with horizontal velocity $e \times (u \cos \theta)$. Hence the time taken by the ball to travel from the wall back to the boy's hand is $\dfrac{a}{eu \cos \theta}$.

Since the time of flight is unchanged

$$\frac{2u \sin \theta}{g} = \frac{a}{u \cos \theta} + \frac{a}{eu \cos \theta}$$

$$= \frac{a}{eu \cos \theta}(1 + e)$$

So:
$$2u^2 \sin \theta \cos \theta = ag \left(\frac{1+e}{e} \right)$$

or:
$$u^2 \sin 2\theta = ag \left(\frac{1+e}{e} \right)$$

Example 9

A golf ball is given an initial speed of u and moves initially in a direction making an angle θ with a smooth horizontal plane. The coefficient of restitution between the ball and the plane is $\frac{1}{4}$. Find:

(a) the horizontal distance travelled by the ball when it strikes the plane for the second time

(b) the total horizontal distance the ball has travelled when it stops bouncing.

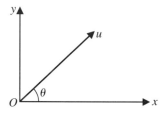

As in the previous example the vertical distance travelled by the ball in time t is given by:

$$y = ut \sin \theta - \tfrac{1}{2}gt^2$$

The first bounce takes place when $y = 0$ and this is at time T_1, the time of flight, where:

$$T_1 = \frac{2u \sin \theta}{g}$$

Since the horizontal velocity remains constant at $u \cos \theta$, the horizontal distance R_1 travelled in this time is

$$R_1 = \left(\frac{2u \sin \theta}{g} \right) \times u \cos \theta$$

$$= \frac{u^2 \sin 2\theta}{g}$$

After the rebound the horizontal velocity is unchanged, and so remains as $u \cos \theta$, and the vertical velocity is now $e \times (u \sin \theta)$ (see chapter 5 of Book M2).

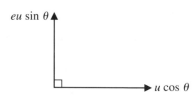

Using the same arguments as before, the time to the next bounce is:

$$T_2 = \frac{2(eu \sin \theta)}{g}$$

and the distance travelled is:

$$R_2 = \left(\frac{2eu \sin \theta}{g} \right) u \cos \theta$$

$$= \frac{eu^2 \sin 2\theta}{g} = eR_1$$

(a) The distance travelled by the ball to the second bounce is:

$$R_1 + R_2 = R_1 + eR_1$$

$$= R_1(1 + e)$$

$$= \frac{u^2 \sin 2\theta}{g}(1 + e)$$

$$= \frac{5}{4g}u^2 \sin 2\theta$$

since $e = \frac{1}{4}$.

(b) Proceeding in the same way, the time between the second and third bounce is:

$$T_3 = \frac{2e^2 u \sin \theta}{g}$$

and the distance is:

$$R_3 = \frac{2e^2 u \sin \theta}{g} u \cos \theta = e^2 R_1$$

So the total distance travelled when the ball stops bouncing is:

$$R = R_1(1 + e + e^2 + \cdots)$$

But $1 + e + e^2 + \cdots$ is a geometric series. The sum to infinity of this series is $\dfrac{1}{1-e}$ (see Book P1 Chapter 6).

Hence:

$$R = \frac{R_1}{1-e} = \frac{u^2 \sin 2\theta}{g\left(1 - \frac{1}{4}\right)} = \frac{4u^2 \sin 2\theta}{3g}$$

The bounding parabola

It is clear from our own experience that when a ball is thrown with a given speed of projection not all points are accessible. It is worthwhile therefore to consider just which points are accessible when the speed of projection is specified.

Suppose the speed of projection is u. Then, if the angle of projection is θ to the horizontal, the horizontal and vertical components of the velocity are $u \cos \theta$ and $u \sin \theta$ respectively.

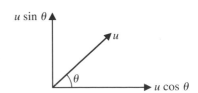

Taking the point of projection as O and the horizontal and vertical axes as Ox and Oy we obtain, using the constant acceleration formulae:

$$x = ut \cos \theta$$

$$y = ut \sin \theta - \tfrac{1}{2} g t^2$$

These are the parametric equations of the trajectory.

The cartesian equation can be obtained by eliminating t.

Thus:
$$t = \frac{x}{u \cos \theta}$$

So:
$$y = \frac{ux \sin \theta}{u \cos \theta} - \tfrac{1}{2} g \frac{x^2}{u^2 \cos^2 \theta}$$

$$y = x \tan \theta - \frac{gx^2}{2u^2} \sec^2 \theta \qquad (1)$$

Equation (1) is the equation of a parabola.

By using $\sec^2 \theta = 1 + \tan^2 \theta$, equation (1) may be written as a quadratic equation in $\tan \theta$:

$$\frac{gx^2}{2u^2} \tan^2 \theta - x \tan \theta + \left(y + \frac{gx^2}{2u^2} \right) = 0 \qquad (2)$$

This can be used to answer the question as to whether a particular point is accessible. Suppose a given point P has coordinates (α, β). Substituting $x = \alpha$ and $y = \beta$ in equation (2) gives:

$$\frac{g\alpha^2}{2u^2} \tan^2 \theta - \alpha \tan \theta + \left(\beta + \frac{g\alpha^2}{2u^2} \right) = 0 \qquad (3)$$

There are three possible outcomes:

 (i) If equation (3), regarded as a quadratic in $\tan \theta$, has real distinct roots then there are two possible paths for the particle from O to P.

 (ii) If equation (3) has equal roots then there is only one possible path from O to P and the point P is the point of maximum range on the line OP.

(iii) If equation (3) has no real roots then the point P cannot be reached by a particle projected with speed u.

The condition for equation (3) to have real roots is that:

$$\alpha^2 \geqslant \frac{4g\alpha^2}{2u^2} \left(\beta + \frac{g\alpha^2}{2u^2} \right)$$

or:
$$\beta \leqslant \frac{u^2}{2g} - \frac{g}{2u^2} \alpha^2$$

Points whose coordinates (α, β) satisfy this inequality are within range of a particle projected with speed u.

From this inequality it can be seen that the curve with equation:

$$y = \frac{u^2}{2g} - \frac{g}{2u^2}x^2 \qquad (4)$$

separates those points which are accessible from O, when the particle has initial speed u, from those which are inaccessible. This curve is called the **bounding parabola**. Points on or below the bounding parabola can be reached but points above it cannot. This situation is illustrated in the diagram.

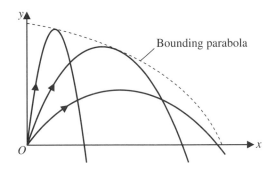

Example 10
A particle P is projected from a point O. A target T is situated at a horizontal distance a from O and at a vertical distance $\frac{3}{4}a$ above the level of O.

  (a) If the initial speed of the particle is $2\sqrt{(ga)}$, find the two possible angles of projection if P is to strike T.
  (b) Find the least possible speed of projection of the particle if it is to reach T.

(a) The two possible values of $\tan \theta$ are obtained from the quadratic equation (3) with $\alpha = a$, $\beta = \frac{3}{4}a$ and $u = \sqrt{ga}$. Substitution of these values gives:

$$\frac{ga^2}{2 \times 4ga}\tan^2 \theta - a\tan \theta + \left(\tfrac{3}{4}a + \frac{ga^2}{2 \times 4ga}\right) = 0$$

Or: $$\frac{a}{8}\tan^2 \theta - a\tan \theta + \frac{7a}{8} = 0$$

So: $$\tan^2 \theta - 8\tan \theta + 7 = 0$$

And: $$(\tan \theta - 7)(\tan \theta - 1) = 0$$

Hence $\tan \theta = 7$ or $\tan \theta = 1$.

So $\theta = \text{arc tan } 7$, or $\theta = \text{arc tan } 1 = \dfrac{\pi}{4}$.

(b) The least possible speed of projection u is obtained when the given point $\left(a, \dfrac{3a}{4}\right)$ lies on the bounding parabola with equation (4).

Hence:

$$\frac{3a}{4} = \frac{u^2}{2g} - \frac{g}{2u^2} a^2$$

Let $\dfrac{u^2}{g} = p$ then:

$$\tfrac{3}{4} a = \frac{p}{2} - \frac{1}{2p} a^2$$

And since p is not zero:

$$3ap = 2p^2 - 2a^2$$

or:

$$2p^2 - 3ap - 2a^2 = 0$$

Factorising:

$$(2p + a)(p - 2a) = 0$$

So $p = -\dfrac{a}{2}$ or $p = 2a$.

The first value is not a possibility as $p > 0$. Hence $p = 2a$.

So:

$$\frac{u^2}{g} = 2a$$

And:

$$u^2 = 2ag$$

Or:

$$u = \sqrt{(2ag)}$$

The least possible value of the speed of projection is $\sqrt{(2ag)}$.

Projectiles on an inclined plane

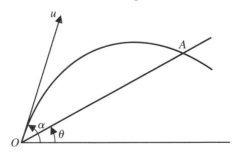

Suppose a particle P is projected from a point O on an inclined plane and that the line of greatest slope of this plane through O makes an angle θ with the horizontal. Assume that the particle is projected in the vertical plane containing this line of greatest slope, that air resistance can be neglected and that g is constant.

Earlier work showed that if the particle is projected with speed u at an angle α to the horizontal it will describe a parabolic path. In this case the particle will only describe the part of the parabola between O and A, where A is the point where the particle strikes the inclined plane. In order to discuss the motion in this case it is more convenient to take axes along and perpendicular to the plane. As a first step, the acceleration due to gravity must be resolved along these axes.

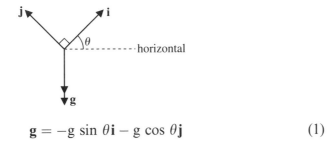

$$\mathbf{g} = -g \sin \theta \mathbf{i} - g \cos \theta \mathbf{j} \qquad (1)$$

Resolving the initial velocity u along these directions gives:

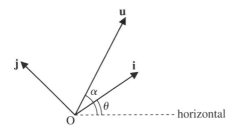

$$\mathbf{u} = u \cos(\alpha - \theta)\mathbf{i} + u \sin(\alpha - \theta)\mathbf{j} \qquad (2)$$

The equation of motion of the particle is:

$$\ddot{\mathbf{r}} = \mathbf{g}$$

Along the plane, that is in the direction of $\mathbf{i}$, from equation (1):

$$\ddot{x} = -g \sin \theta$$

Integrating with respect to t gives:

$$\dot{x} = -gt \sin \theta + c_1$$

Using (2) gives:

$$u \cos(\alpha - \theta) = c_1$$

So: $$\dot{x} = -gt \sin \theta + u \cos(\alpha - \theta)$$

Integrating again with respect to t gives:

$$x = ut \cos(\alpha - \theta) - \tfrac{1}{2} gt^2 \sin \theta + c_2$$

Measuring x and y from the point of projection, $x = 0$ at $t = 0$ so $c_2 = 0$ and:

$$x = ut \cos(\alpha - \theta) - \tfrac{1}{2} gt^2 \sin \theta \qquad (3)$$

Perpendicular to the plane, that is in the direction of $\mathbf{j}$, from (1):

$$\ddot{y} = -g \cos \theta$$

Integrating with respect to t and using (2) gives:

$$\dot{y} = -gt \cos \theta + u \sin (\alpha - \theta)$$

A further integration with respect to t and use of the initial conditions gives:

$$y = ut \sin(\alpha - \theta) - \tfrac{1}{2} gt^2 \cos \theta \qquad (4)$$

It is not suggested that these equations be memorised but rather the method of derivation should be understood starting from the equation of motion $\ddot{\mathbf{r}} = \mathbf{g}$.

Time of flight

The particle strikes the plane at A that is when $y = 0$. This simple equation is one reason why the choice of axes made is particularly appropriate.

When $y = 0$:

$$t \left[u \sin(\alpha - \theta) - \tfrac{1}{2} gt \cos \theta \right] = 0$$

So: $\qquad\qquad\qquad t = 0$, (initially)

Or: $\qquad\qquad\qquad t = \dfrac{2u \sin(\alpha - \theta)}{g \cos \theta}$

■ $T = 2u \dfrac{\sin(\alpha - \theta)}{g \cos \theta}$ **is the time of flight from O to P.**

Range on the plane

The range on the plane is OA. This is the value of x when t is the time of flight T obtained above.

When $t = \dfrac{2u \sin(\alpha - \theta)}{g \cos \theta}$

$$x = u \cos(\alpha - \theta)\frac{2u \sin(\alpha - \theta)}{g \cos \theta} - \tfrac{1}{2}g \sin \theta \left[\frac{4u^2 \sin^2(\alpha - \theta)}{g^2 \cos^2 \theta} \right]$$

$$= \frac{2u^2 \sin(\alpha - \theta)}{g \cos^2 \theta} [\cos \theta \cos(\alpha - \theta) - \sin \theta \sin(\alpha - \theta)]$$

$$= \frac{2u^2 \sin(\alpha - \theta) \cos \alpha}{g \cos^2 \theta}$$

■ **The range R on the inclined plane is:**

$$\frac{2u^2 \sin(\alpha - \theta) \cos \alpha}{g \cos^2 \theta}$$

Maximum range on the plane

It is useful to know the maximum range on the plane for a given speed. Remember that θ, the angle of the plane, is fixed. So we require the maximum value of R as α varies.

The terms involving α in the above formula for R are $\sin(\alpha - \theta)\cos\alpha$.

Recall that: $\sin A \cos B = \frac{1}{2}[\sin(A+B) + \sin(A-B)]$

So: $\sin(\alpha - \theta)\cos\alpha = \frac{1}{2}[\sin(2\alpha - \theta) + \sin(-\theta)]$

$$= \frac{1}{2}[\sin(2\alpha - \theta) - \sin\theta]$$

Hence R is a maximum when $\sin(2\alpha - \theta)$ is a maximum, that is when

$2\alpha - \theta = \dfrac{\pi}{2}$ and $\sin(2\alpha - \theta) = 1$.

So $\alpha = \frac{1}{4}\pi + \frac{1}{2}\theta$.

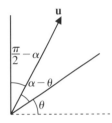

When: $\alpha = \dfrac{\pi}{4} + \dfrac{1}{2}\theta$

Then: $\alpha - \theta = \dfrac{\pi}{4} - \dfrac{\theta}{2}$

And: $\dfrac{\pi}{2} - \alpha = \dfrac{\pi}{4} - \dfrac{\theta}{2}$

This means the range on the plane is maximum when the direction of projection bisects the angle between the inclined plane and the vertical.

The maximum range on the plane is:

$$R_{\max} = \frac{2u^2\left(\frac{1}{2}\right)(1 - \sin\theta)}{g\cos^2\theta}$$

As $\cos^2\theta = 1 - \sin^2\theta$ this may be simplified to:

$$R_{\max} = \frac{u^2}{g(1 + \sin\theta)}$$

Projection down the plane can be treated in a similar manner. In this discussion the direction of projection was expressed as an elevation to the horizontal. This direction could also have been given relative to the inclined plane.

When solving problems, read the question very carefully to establish which of these angles is given.

Example 11

A particle is projected with speed u from a point O at the foot of a plane of inclination θ. The direction of projection lies in the vertical plane containing the line of greatest slope through O and makes an angle α with the horizontal. Neglecting air resistance, show that if the particle strikes the plane at right angles then:

$$1 + 2 \tan^2 \theta = \tan \alpha \tan \theta$$

The information given is summarised in the diagram.

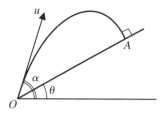
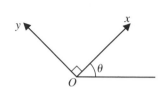

As before, take axes along and perpendicular to the plane.

(i) When the particle strikes the plane at A, $y = 0$.

(ii) Since the particle strikes the plane at right angles at the point A, the velocity has no component along the plane, that is $\dot{x} = 0$, at this point.

Perpendicular to plane	Along plane

Perpendicular to plane

$\ddot{y} = -g \cos \theta$
$\dot{y} = -gt \cos \theta + u \sin(\alpha - \theta)$
$y = ut \sin(\alpha - \theta) - \frac{1}{2} gt^2 \cos \theta$

Along plane

$\ddot{x} = -g \sin \theta$
$\dot{x} = -gt \sin \theta + u \cos(\alpha - \theta)$

(i) $y = 0$ at $A \Rightarrow ut \sin(\alpha - \theta) - \frac{1}{2} gt^2 \cos \theta = 0$

So $t = 0$ or $t = \dfrac{2u \sin(\alpha - \theta)}{g \cos \theta}$

(ii) $\dot{x} = 0$ at $A \Rightarrow -gt \sin \theta + u \cos(\alpha - \theta) = 0$

So $t = \dfrac{u \cos(\alpha - \theta)}{g \sin \theta}$

Equating these two results for t gives:

$$\frac{2u \sin(\alpha - \theta)}{g \cos \theta} = \frac{u \cos(\alpha - \theta)}{g \sin \theta}$$

Or: $\qquad 2 \sin(\alpha - \theta) \sin \theta = \cos(\alpha - \theta) \cos \theta$

So: $\qquad \tan(\alpha - \theta) = \frac{1}{2} \cot \theta$

Using the formula for $\tan(A - B)$ (see **Book P1** chapter 7) gives:

$$\frac{\tan \alpha - \tan \theta}{1 + \tan \theta \tan \alpha} = \frac{1}{2} \cot \theta$$

So: $\qquad 2 \tan \theta \tan \alpha - 2 \tan^2 \theta = 1 + \tan \theta \tan \alpha$

And: $\qquad 1 + 2 \tan^2 \theta = \tan \alpha \tan \theta$

Example 12

A particle is projected from a point A on a smooth plane of inclination θ and strikes the plane at the point B, where AB is a line of greatest slope and B is above A. The particle is projected in a vertical plane with velocity V at an angle β with the plane.

The coefficient of restitution between the particle and the plane is e. Given that when the particle strikes the plane at B it rebounds in a vertical direction, show that:

$$e + 2 = \cot \theta \cot \beta$$

Notice that in this problem the direction of the initial velocity is given *relative to the plane*.

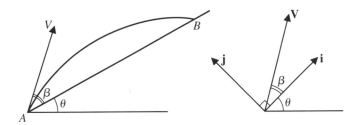

Begin by drawing a diagram summarising the given information.
As before $\mathbf{g} = -g \sin \theta \mathbf{i} - g \cos \theta \mathbf{j}$, but now $\mathbf{V} = V \cos \beta \mathbf{i} + V \sin \beta \mathbf{j}$.

The equation of motion perpendicular to the plane is:

$$\ddot{y} = -g \cos \theta$$

Integrating with respect to t:

$$\dot{y} = -gt \cos \theta + V \sin \beta$$

Integrating again:

$$y = Vt \sin \beta - \tfrac{1}{2} gt^2 \cos \theta$$

The time T taken to reach B is obtained from $y = 0$ and so:

$$T = \frac{2V \sin \beta}{g \cos \theta}$$

The equation of motion along the plane is:

$$\ddot{x} = -g \sin \theta$$

Integrating: $\qquad \dot{x} = -gt \sin \theta + V \cos \beta.$

The components of the velocity when the particle reaches B are:

$$\dot{x}(T) = -g \sin \theta \frac{2V \sin \beta}{g \cos \theta} + V \cos \beta$$

$$= -2V \tan \theta \sin \beta + V \cos \beta$$

And:
$$\dot{y}(T) = -g \cos \theta \frac{2V \sin \beta}{g \cos \theta} + V \sin \beta$$
$$= -2V \sin \beta + V \sin \beta = -V \sin \beta$$

The equation for $\dot{y}$ shows that the particle reaches the plane with the same normal velocity as it had initially.

The particle will rebound from the plane with normal velocity $eV \sin \beta$. The velocity along the plane is unchanged by the impact.

After the impact:

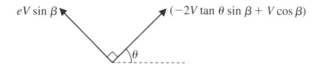

As the particle rebounds in a vertical direction, the horizontal component of the velocity is zero. So:
$$eV \sin \beta \sin \theta = (-2V \tan \theta \sin \beta + V \cos \beta) \cos \theta$$
$$= -2V \sin \theta \sin \beta + V \cos \beta \cos \theta$$

Dividing by $V \sin \theta \sin \beta$ gives
$$e + 2 = \cot \beta \cot \theta$$

Exercise 3C

1 An elastic particle is initially at a height h above horizontal ground and at a distance a from a smooth vertical wall. The ball is projected horizontally towards the wall with speed u. Given that $a < u\sqrt{\left(\dfrac{2h}{g}\right)}$ and that the coefficient of restitution between the particle and the wall is e, show that the particle strikes the ground at a distance:
$$e\left[u\sqrt{\left(\frac{2h}{g}\right)} - a\right]$$
from the wall.

2 A ball is projected from ground level in a room with a smooth horizontal ceiling at height h. The ball is projected with speed $3\sqrt{(gh)}$ in a direction making an angle of $45°$ with the horizontal. The coefficient of restitution between the ball and the ceiling is $\frac{1}{2}$.

Show that the angle made with the horizontal by its trajectory on its return to the floor is

$$\arctan\left(\sqrt{\tfrac{7}{12}}\right)$$

3 An elastic particle is projected with speed u at angle of elevation θ from a point O of a smooth horizontal floor. It is directed towards a smooth vertical wall at a distance d away and rebounds to strike the floor for the first time at O. It then rebounds from the floor and next strikes it at the point B. Show that the distance $OB = de(1 + e)$ where e is the coefficient of restitution between the ball and the wall and the ball and the floor.

4 A ball which is thrown with initial speed $\sqrt{(2gh)}$ strikes a smooth vertical wall, which is perpendicular to its plane of motion, and stands at a distance d from the point of projection. Show that the point A at which the ball strikes the wall cannot be at a height greater than

$$\frac{(4h^2 - d^2)}{4h}$$

above the point of projection.

5 A stone is projected from the point O with speed $4\sqrt{(2ga)}$ and passes through the point with coordinates $(24a, 3a)$ where the x and y axes are horizontal and vertical respectively. Find the possible angles of projection.

6 A gun fires a shell with velocity V at an angle of elevation θ to hit an aeroplane which flies overhead at a constant height h (where $h < V^2/2g$) above the ground. If x is the horizontal distance from the gun, obtain the quadratic equation in x whose two solutions are the distances at which the aeroplane can be hit.

7 A particle is projected from a point O so as to just pass over a wall of height h. The **top** of the wall is at a distance r from the point of projection.

(a) Show that the least speed of projection so that this may happen is $\sqrt{[g(h + r)]}$.

(b) Show also that with this speed the particle will have reached its maximum height before grazing the wall.

(c) Show that the corresponding angle of projection is:

$$\arctan \sqrt{\left(\frac{r+h}{r-h}\right)}$$

8 A particle is projected with speed u from a point on a plane of slope β. Show that the maximum range down the plane is:

$$\frac{u^2}{g(1-\sin\beta)}$$

9 A particle is projected with speed $90\,\text{ms}^{-1}$ at an inclination of $60°$ to the horizontal on a plane inclined at $30°$ to the same horizontal. The motion takes place in a vertical plane through a line of greatest slope of the plane. Find
(a) the range on the plane,
(b) the time of flight of the particle.

10 A particle is projected with a speed of $21\,\text{ms}^{-1}$ from a point O in a plane inclined at an angle of $30°$ to the horizontal. Calculate the maximum range of the particle
(a) up the plane,
(b) down the plane.

11 A particle is projected from a point O on a plane inclined at an angle θ to the horizontal. The maximum range up the plane is R and the corresponding time of flight is T. Show that

$$R = \tfrac{1}{2} g T^2$$

12 A particle is fired with speed u at an angle of elevation of $(\alpha + \theta)$ above the horizontal from a point O in a plane inclined at an angle θ to the horizontal. The motion takes place in a vertical plane through the line of greatest slope. The particle is moving horizontally when it strikes the slope. Show that

$$\tan \alpha = \frac{\sin \theta \cos \theta}{1 + \sin^2\theta}$$

13 The point O lies on a smooth plane inclined at an angle θ to the horizontal. A ball is projected from O with speed u in a direction making an angle β to the plane and $\theta + \beta$ to the horizontal. The ball returns to O on the nth bounce. Show that

$$\cot \theta \cot \beta = \frac{1 - e^n}{1 - e}$$

where e is the coefficient of restitution between the plane and the ball.

SUMMARY OF KEY POINTS

1 When a particle, of mass m, moves on a plane curve, with intrinsic equation $s = \mathrm{f}(\psi)$, under a force

$$\mathbf{F} = S\hat{\mathbf{s}} + N\hat{\mathbf{n}}$$

where $\hat{\mathbf{s}}$ and $\hat{\mathbf{n}}$ are unit vectors along the tangent and the normal, the equations of motion are:

tangential: $\qquad\qquad m\dot{v} = S$

normal: $\qquad\qquad \dfrac{mv^2}{\rho} = N$

2 When a particle, of mass m, moves in a plane under the action of a central force, of magnitude $\mathrm{f}(r)$, towards O, the centre of force, the equations of motion are:

radial: $\qquad m\left(\ddot{r} - r\dot{\theta}^2\right) = -\mathrm{f}(r)$

transverse: $\qquad \dfrac{m}{r}\dfrac{\mathrm{d}}{\mathrm{d}t}\left(r^2\dot{\theta}\right) = 0$

3 When a particle moves under a central force its moment of momentum about the centre of the force remains constant. That is $r^2\dot{\theta} = h$, where h is constant.

Review exercise

1 [*In this question the velocities given are relative to the earth. The unit vectors* **i** *and* **j** *are directed due east and due north respectively.*]

A helicopter pilot is informed that a lifeboat is drifting in the sea with velocity $(-2\mathbf{i} + 4\mathbf{j})\,\text{km h}^{-1}$ and that, relative to his position, the lifeboat has position vector $5(2\mathbf{i} + \mathbf{j})\,\text{km}$. The helicopter is travelling at its maximum speed of $100\,\text{km h}^{-1}$ and the pilot immediately moves to intercept the lifeboat in the shortest possible time. Given that the constant velocity of the helicopter is $(u\mathbf{i} + v\mathbf{j})\,\text{km h}^{-1}$ show that

(a) $u = 2v - 10$.

(b) $v^2 - 8v - 1980 = 0$.

(c) Calculate the time taken by the helicopter to reach the lifeboat giving your answer to the nearest one-tenth of a minute.

(d) Calculate the bearing of the course taken by the helicopter giving your answer to the nearest one-tenth of a degree.   [L]

2 At time t two points P and Q have position vectors **p** and **q** respectively, where

$$\mathbf{p} = 2a\mathbf{i} + (a \cos \omega t)\mathbf{j} + (a \sin \omega t)\mathbf{k},$$

$$\mathbf{q} = (a \sin \omega t)\mathbf{i} - (a \cos \omega t)\mathbf{j} + 3a\mathbf{k}$$

and a, ω are constants. Find **r**, the position vector of P relative to Q, and **v**, the velocity of P relative to Q. Find also the values of t for which **r** and **v** are perpendicular.

Determine the smallest and greatest distances between P and Q.
      [L]

3 A rugby player is running due north with speed $4\,\text{m s}^{-1}$. He throws the ball horizontally and the ball has an initial velocity

relative to the player of $6\,\mathrm{m\,s^{-1}}$ in the direction $\theta°$ west of south, i.e. on a bearing of $(180 + \theta)°$, where $\tan\theta° = \frac{4}{3}$. Find the magnitude and the direction of the initial velocity of the ball relative to a stationary spectator.

Find also the bearing on which the ball appears to move initially to the referee who is running with speed $2\sqrt{2}\,\mathrm{m\,s^{-1}}$ in a north-westerly direction.

(Give all results to 3 significant figures, with bearings in degrees.)

[L]

4 A river flows at a constant speed of $5\,\mathrm{m\,s^{-1}}$ between straight parallel banks which are 240 m apart. A boat crosses the river, travelling relative to the water at a constant speed of $12\,\mathrm{m\,s^{-1}}$. A man cycles at a constant speed of $4\,\mathrm{m\,s^{-1}}$ along the edge of one bank of the river in the direction opposite to the direction of flow of the river. At the instant when the boat leaves a point O on the opposite bank, the cyclist is 80 m downstream of O. The boat is steered relative to the water in a direction perpendicular to the banks. Taking $\mathbf{i}$ and $\mathbf{j}$ to be perpendicular horizontal unit vectors downstream and across the river from O respectively, express, in terms of $\mathbf{i}$ and $\mathbf{j}$, the velocities and the position vectors relative to O of the boat and the cyclist t seconds after the boat leaves O. Hence, or otherwise, calculate the time when the distance between the boat and the cyclist is least, giving this least distance. If, instead, the boat were to be steered so that it crosses the river from O to a point on the other bank directly opposite to O, show that this crossing would take approximately 22 seconds.

[L]

5 The unit vectors $\mathbf{i}$ and $\mathbf{j}$ are directed due East and due North respectively. The airport B is due north of airport A. On a particular day the velocity of the wind is $(70\mathbf{i} + 25\mathbf{j})\,\mathrm{km\,h^{-1}}$. Relative to the air an aircraft flies with constant speed $250\,\mathrm{km\,h^{-1}}$. When the aircraft flies directly from A to B determine
(a) its speed, in $\mathrm{km\,h^{-1}}$ relative to the ground
(b) the direction, to the nearest degree, in which it must head.
After flying from A to B, the aircraft returns directly to A.
(c) Calculate the ratio of the time taken on the outward flight to the time taken on the return flight.

[L]

6 At time $t = 0$, a particle A, which moves with constant velocity
   $(3\mathbf{i} + u\mathbf{j} + 5\mathbf{k})\,\mathrm{m\,s^{-1}}$, has position vector $(4\mathbf{i} + 9\mathbf{j} - 10\mathbf{k})\,\mathrm{m}$
   relative to a fixed origin O. At time $t = 0$, a particle B, which has
   constant velocity $2\mathbf{i}\,\mathrm{m\,s^{-1}}$, is at O.
   (a) Given that $u = 2$, find the value of t at the instant when the
   distance between A and B is least.
   (b) At time t s, a third particle C has position vector

   $$[10\mathbf{i} + 5\mathbf{j}\ \sin(\pi t/4) + 5\mathbf{k}\ \cos(\pi t/4)]\,\mathrm{m}$$

   relative to the fixed origin O. Find the value of u in this case,
   given that A and C collide.   [L]

7 At time t a particle P, of mass m, has position vector $\mathbf{p}$, given by

   $$\mathbf{p} = (3a\ \cos\ \omega t)\mathbf{i} + (4a\ \sin\ \omega t)\mathbf{j}$$

   where a and ω are positive constants. Find, in terms of m, a, ω
   and t
   (a) the kinetic energy of P
   (b) the magnitude of the force acting on P.
   A second particle Q has position vector $\mathbf{q}$, given by

   $$\mathbf{q} = (3a\ \sin\ \omega t)\mathbf{j} + (4a\ \cos\ \omega t)\mathbf{k}$$

   Find $\mathbf{r}$ the position vector of P relative to Q.
   Evaluate $\mathbf{r}\,.\,\mathbf{r}$ and hence, or otherwise, show that the greatest and
   least distances between P and Q are $5a$ and a respectively.   [L]

8 Solve the vector differential equation

   $$\frac{d^2\mathbf{r}}{d\theta^2} = \frac{d\mathbf{r}}{d\theta}.$$

   given that $\dfrac{d\mathbf{r}}{d\theta} = \mathbf{i}$ and $\mathbf{r} = \mathbf{j}$ when $\theta = 0$.   [L]

9 Find the general solution of the vector differential equation

   $$\frac{d^2\mathbf{r}}{d\theta^2} - 2\frac{d\mathbf{r}}{d\theta} + 10\mathbf{r} = 0$$

   Given that $\mathbf{r} = \mathbf{j}$ when $\theta = 0$, find $\mathbf{r}$ when $\theta = \pi$.   [L]

10 At time t, the velocity $\mathbf{v}$ of a particle P satisfies the vector
   differential equation

   $$\frac{d\mathbf{v}}{dt} + \frac{3\mathbf{v}}{T} = 0$$

where T is a constant. At time $t = 0$, the position vector of P is $a(\mathbf{i} + 2\mathbf{j})$ and its velocity is $3a(\mathbf{i} - \mathbf{j})/T$.

Find the position vector of P at any time t.   [L]

11 Integrate the vector equation

$$\frac{d^2\mathbf{r}}{dt^2} + n^2\mathbf{r} = 0$$

to find $\mathbf{r}$, given that $\mathbf{r} = (\mathbf{i} + \mathbf{j})\,a$ and $\dfrac{d\mathbf{r}}{dt} = (\mathbf{i} - 2\mathbf{k})b$ when $t = 0$.

[L]

12 Solve the differential equation

$$\frac{d\mathbf{r}}{dt} = 2\mathbf{r}$$

given that, when $t = 0$ $\mathbf{r} \cdot \mathbf{j} = 0$ and $\mathbf{r} \times \mathbf{j} = \mathbf{i} + \mathbf{k}$.   [L]

13 At time t the position vector $\mathbf{r}$ of the point P satisfies the differential equation

$$\frac{d^2\mathbf{r}}{dt^2} - 9w^2\mathbf{r} = \mathbf{i}aw^2 \sin 2wt$$

where w and a are constants. When $t = 0$, P passes with velocity $wa\mathbf{i}$ through the point with position vector $a\mathbf{j}$. Find a vector equation of the locus of P.   [L]

14 Find the work done by a constant force $\mathbf{F}$, where

$$\mathbf{F} = (6\mathbf{i} + 2\mathbf{j} - \mathbf{k})\,\mathrm{N}$$

when the point of application is moved from the point with position vector $\mathbf{a}$ to the point with position vector $\mathbf{b}$, where

$\mathbf{a} = (\mathbf{i} + \mathbf{j} + 4\mathbf{k})\,\mathrm{m}$
and $\mathbf{b} = (3\mathbf{i} - 3\mathbf{j} + 3\mathbf{k})\,\mathrm{m}$ [L]

15 Find the work done by a force $\mathbf{F}$, where

$$\mathbf{F} = (3\mathbf{i} + 5\mathbf{j} + 4\mathbf{k})\,\mathrm{N},$$

when the point of application is moved from the point with position vector $\mathbf{a}$ to the point with position vector $\mathbf{b}$, where,

$$\mathbf{a} = (2\mathbf{i} + 3\mathbf{j} - 3\mathbf{k})\,\mathrm{m} \quad \mathbf{b} = (5\mathbf{i} + \mathbf{j} - \mathbf{k})\,\mathrm{m} \qquad [L]$$

16 Find the work done by a force $\mathbf{F}$ where

$$\mathbf{F} = (16\mathbf{i} + 12\mathbf{j})\,\mathrm{N}$$

when the point of application is moved from the point with
position vector **a** to the point with position vector **b**, where

$$\mathbf{a} = (-2\mathbf{i} + \mathbf{j} + \mathbf{k})\,\mathrm{m} \quad \text{and} \quad \mathbf{b} = (10\mathbf{i} + 5\mathbf{j} + 11\mathbf{k})\,\mathrm{m} \quad [\mathrm{L}]$$

17 A force **F** of magnitude 18 N acts along the direction of the
vector $(7\mathbf{i} + 4\mathbf{j} + 4\mathbf{k})$. A bead moves along a smooth straight
wire from the point A to the point B, where A and B have
position vectors

$$(\mathbf{i} + 3\mathbf{j} - 2\mathbf{k})\,\mathrm{m} \quad \text{and} \quad (3\mathbf{i} + 5\mathbf{j} - \mathbf{k})\,\mathrm{m}$$

respectively, under the action of **F** and the reaction **R** of the wire
only. Find **R** and the work done by **F** in the motion.   [L]

18 The line of action of a force $2\mathbf{i} - \mathbf{j} + 3\mathbf{k}$ passes through the
origin and the line of action of a second force $\mathbf{i} + 2\mathbf{j} - \mathbf{k}$ passes
through the point $(-1, 2, -3)$. Reduce the two forces to a single
force acting at the origin together with a couple.   [L]

19 Forces $4\mathbf{j}$ N, $3\mathbf{k}$ N act through the points with position vectors
$(\mathbf{i} + \mathbf{k})\,\mathrm{m}$ and $(\mathbf{i} + \mathbf{j})\,\mathrm{m}$ respectively. A third force acts through
the point with position vector $(\mathbf{j} + \mathbf{k})\,\mathrm{m}$ and is such that the three
forces are equivalent to a couple. Find the vector moment and
the magnitude of this couple.   [L]

20 The forces $(b\mathbf{j} + c\mathbf{k})$, $(c\mathbf{k} + a\mathbf{i})$ and $(a\mathbf{i} + b\mathbf{j})$ act respectively
through the three points with position vectors $a\mathbf{i}$, $b\mathbf{j}$ and $c\mathbf{k}$, where
a, b and c are constants. Show that the force system is equivalent
to a single force through the origin and find its magnitude.   [L]

21 Forces $\mathbf{F}_1$ and $\mathbf{F}_2$, where

$$\mathbf{F}_1 = (3\mathbf{i} + 7\mathbf{j} + 5\mathbf{k})\,\mathrm{N}, \quad \mathbf{F}_2 = (2\mathbf{i} - 3\mathbf{j} + \mathbf{k})\,\mathrm{N}$$

act respectively through points whose position vectors with
respect to an origin O are $\mathbf{r}_1$ and $\mathbf{r}_2$, where

$$\mathbf{r}_1 = (4\mathbf{i} + 9\mathbf{j} + 8\mathbf{k})\,\mathrm{m}, \quad \mathbf{r}_2 = (-3\mathbf{i} + 8\mathbf{j} + \mathbf{k})\,\mathrm{m}$$

Show that the lines of action of the forces $\mathbf{F}_1$ and $\mathbf{F}_2$ meet at a
point, and find the position vector of this point of intersection.
A third force, $\mathbf{F}_3$, where $\mathbf{F}_3 = (4\mathbf{i} + 2\mathbf{j} + 3\mathbf{k})\,\mathrm{N}$, acts through the
point with position vector $(a\mathbf{i} + b\mathbf{j} + 3\mathbf{k})\,\mathrm{m}$. Given that the
system of forces $\mathbf{F}_1$, $\mathbf{F}_2$ and $\mathbf{F}_3$ can be represented by a single
force **F** acting through the origin, find the values of the constants
a and b.   [L]

22 A force $\mathbf{F}_1$, of magnitude 26 N, acts along the direction of the vector $(4\mathbf{i} - 3\mathbf{j} + 12\mathbf{k})$. Given that the line of action of $\mathbf{F}_1$ passes through the point which has position vector $(2\mathbf{i} + \mathbf{j} - \mathbf{k})$ m, find the moment of $\mathbf{F}_1$ about the origin O.

A bead moves along a smooth straight wire from the point A to the point B, where

$$\overrightarrow{OA} = (3\mathbf{i} - 2\mathbf{j} + \mathbf{k})\,\text{m}, \quad \overrightarrow{OB} = (5\mathbf{i} - 22\mathbf{j} + 2\mathbf{k})\,\text{m}$$

under the influence of $\mathbf{F}_1$ and the reaction of the wire only. Find the work done by $\mathbf{F}_1$ in this motion.

Two other forces $\mathbf{F}_2$ and $\mathbf{F}_3$ of magnitudes 7 N and 9 N, act along the directions of the vectors $(2\mathbf{i} - 6\mathbf{j} + 3\mathbf{k})$ and $(-4\mathbf{i} + 7\mathbf{j} - 4\mathbf{k})$ respectively. Given that both $\mathbf{F}_2$ and $\mathbf{F}_3$ pass through the point with position vector $(\mathbf{i} + \mathbf{j} + \mathbf{k})$ m, reduce the three forces $\mathbf{F}_1$, $\mathbf{F_2}$ and $\mathbf{F}_3$ to a single force at O and a couple.

[L]

23 Define the moment about a point O of a force $\mathbf{F}$ with point of application P such that $\overrightarrow{OP} = \mathbf{r}$. Show that $\mathbf{F}$ can be considered to act at any point on its line of action without changing the moment. Forces $\mathbf{F}_1$, $\mathbf{F}_2$, where $\mathbf{F}_1 = 2\lambda\mathbf{i}$, $\mathbf{F}_2 = -3\lambda\mathbf{j}$, act at the origin O and a force $\mathbf{F_3}$, where $\mathbf{F}_3 = \lambda\mathbf{i} - \lambda\mathbf{j}$, acts at the point with position vector $a(\mathbf{i} + \mathbf{j})$, where a and λ are positive constants. Find

(a) the magnitude of the single resultant force $\mathbf{R}$ of the system,

(b) the moment of the forces $\mathbf{F}_1$, $\mathbf{F}_2$, and $\mathbf{F}_3$ about O.

By assuming $\mathbf{R}$ to act at a point with position vector $a(x\mathbf{i} + y\mathbf{j})$ find the moment of $\mathbf{R}$ about O and hence deduce the equation of the line of action of $\mathbf{R}$.

[L]

24 Forces, $\mathbf{F}_1$, $\mathbf{F_2}$, $\mathbf{F}_3$, where

$$\mathbf{F}_1 = (3\mathbf{i} - \mathbf{j} + 2\mathbf{k})\,\text{N},$$
$$\mathbf{F}_2 = (-\mathbf{i} - 4\mathbf{j} + \mathbf{k})\,\text{N},$$
$$\mathbf{F}_3 = (\mathbf{i} + \mathbf{j} - 2\mathbf{k})\,\text{N},$$

act at points with position vectors $\mathbf{r}_1$, $\mathbf{r}_2$, $\mathbf{r}_3$, where

$$\mathbf{r}_1 = (6\mathbf{i} - \mathbf{j} + \mathbf{k})\,\text{m},$$
$$\mathbf{r}_2 = (\mathbf{i} - 8\mathbf{j} + \mathbf{k})\,\text{m},$$
$$\mathbf{r}_3 = (\mathbf{i} - 2\mathbf{j} + 3\mathbf{k})\,\text{m}.$$

When a fourth force $\mathbf{F}_4$ is added to these three forces, the system is in equilibrium. Find $\mathbf{F}_4$ and a vector equation of its line of action.

Find also the moment of $\mathbf{F}_4$ about the origin O.

25 A rigid body is acted on by a force $\mathbf{F}_1$ at the point with position vector $\mathbf{r}_1$ and by a force $\mathbf{F}_2$ at the point with position vector $\mathbf{r}_2$ where

$$\begin{aligned}
\mathbf{F}_1 &= (-7\mathbf{i} + \mathbf{j} + 2\mathbf{k})\,\text{N}, \\
\mathbf{F}_2 &= (4\mathbf{i} - 3\mathbf{j} + 2\mathbf{k})\,\text{N}, \\
\mathbf{r}_1 &= (-2\mathbf{i} + 4\mathbf{j})\,\text{m} \\
\mathbf{r}_2 &= (9\mathbf{i})\,\text{m}.
\end{aligned}$$

A third force $\mathbf{F}_3$ also acts on the body.

Given that the body is in equilibrium under the action of the three forces, find $\mathbf{F}_3$ and show that the vector equation of the line of action of $\mathbf{F}_3$ may be written in the form

$$\mathbf{r} = [(5\mathbf{i} + 3\mathbf{j} - 2\mathbf{k}) + s(3\mathbf{i} + 2\mathbf{j} - 4\mathbf{k})]\,\text{m},$$

where s is a parameter. [L]

26 A smooth wire is in the shape of the curve with equation

$$y = \ln\,[\sec\,x], \quad 0 \leqslant x \leqslant \frac{\pi}{3}$$

The wire is fixed in a vertical plane with the y-axis vertical. A small bead, of mass m, can move on the wire. It starts from rest at the point $x = \frac{\pi}{3}$ and slides down the wire.

(a) Obtain the magnitude of the normal contact force exerted by the wire on the bead at the point where $x = \alpha$, $\left(0 < \alpha < \frac{\pi}{3} \right)$

Given that the bead reaches the origin with speed v,

(b) show that the normal contact force exerted on the bead at the origin is of magnitude $mv^2 + mg$.

27 A particle P slides down a smooth curve, fixed in a vertical plane, which is bent into the form of the catenary

$$y = a \cosh\left(\frac{x}{a}\right)$$

the y-axis being vertically downwards.

The particle is just disturbed from its highest point. Show that it leaves the curve at the point where the tangent makes an angle of $\dfrac{\pi}{3}$ with the horizontal.

28 A smooth plane curve, in the shape of an arch of the cycloid $s = 4a \sin \psi$, $\left(-\dfrac{\pi}{2} < \psi < \dfrac{\pi}{2}\right)$ is fixed in a vertical plane with its vertex O at its lowest point. Show that the time taken for a particle P to slide from rest at any point on the curve to O is independent of the initial position of P.

29 A smooth plane curve in the shape of an arch of the cycloid $s = 4a \sin \psi$, $\left(-\dfrac{\pi}{2} < \psi < \dfrac{\pi}{2}\right)$ is fixed in a vertical plane with its vertex O at its highest point. A particle P is slightly disturbed from rest at O. Show that the particle will leave the curve when its vertical displacement from O is a.

30 A satellite S, of mass m, is orbiting about Venus in a plane through the centre O of Venus which may be regarded as stationary. The only force on the satellite has magnitude F and acts along SO. At time t, OS is of length r and is rotating about O with angular speed $\dot{\theta}$. When $t = 0$, $r = a$ and the satellite is moving with speed V in a direction perpendicular to OS.

(a) Show that $r^2\dot{\theta} = aV$

Given that $F = \dfrac{2maV^2}{r^2}$,

(b) show that $\ddot{r} = \dfrac{aV^2(a - 2r)}{r^3}$

(c) Hence show that

$$\dot{r}^2 = \dfrac{V^2}{r^2}(4ar - a^2 - 3r^2)$$

(d) Deduce that the satellite is also moving in a direction perpendicular to OS when $r = \frac{1}{3}a$. [L]

31 A particle P moving in a plane has polar coordinates (r, θ) referred to the pole O and an initial line in the plane. Prove that the radial and transverse components of the acceleration of P are respectively $(\ddot{r} - r\dot{\theta}^2)$ and $\dfrac{1}{r}\dfrac{\mathrm{d}}{\mathrm{d}t}\left(r^2\dot{\theta}\right)$.

A particle moves on the curve with polar equation

$$r = 5ke^{\theta}$$

where k is a constant.

When the particle is at a distance r from the pole, its radial component of velocity is $\dfrac{3k^2}{rT}$, where T is a constant. Find in terms of k, r and T the magnitude and direction of the acceleration of the particle. [L]

32 A particle P, of mass m, is moving under the action of a force F in a plane which contains the point O. The force acts along PO and has magnitude $m\,\dfrac{V^2a^3}{r^4}$ where V and a are constants and $r = OP$.

When $t = 0$, P is projected from a point at a distance a from O with speed $\dfrac{V}{\sqrt{6}}$ in a direction perpendicular to OP. Given that θ is the angle between the line OP at time t and its position when $t = 0$ show that

(a) $r^2\dot{\theta} = a\,\dfrac{V}{\sqrt{6}}$

(b) $\ddot{r} = \dfrac{V^2a^2}{6r^4}(r - 6a)$

(c) $\dot{r}^2 = \dfrac{V^2(4a^3 - a^2r - 3r^3)}{6r^3}$.

Show further that, in the subsequent motion, r never exceeds a. Find the distance of the particle from O when the speed is V. [L]

33 A particle P, of unit mass, moves in a plane curve. At time t, P is at the point with polar coordinates (r, θ) referred to pole O.

(a) Derive expressions for the components of the acceleration of P along and perpendicular to the radius vector OP.

A bead Q of unit mass, is threaded on a straight smooth wire passing through O. The wire is made to rotate in a horizontal plane about a vertical axis through O with constant angular speed ω. The bead moves under the action of a force of magnitude $2w^2(r - a)$, where a is a constant, directed towards O. When $\theta = 0$, $r = 3a$ and the radial component of velocity is zero.

(b) Show that

$$\dot{r}^2 = w^2(4ar - 3a^2 - r^2).$$

(c) Hence, or otherwise, find in terms of a, the polar equation of the path of Q. [L]

34 A particle P moving in a plane has polar coordinates (r, θ) referred to the fixed pole O and a fixed initial line in the plane. The radial and transverse components of the velocity of P at time t are $c \tan \left(\frac{1}{2}\theta\right)$ and c respectively, where c is a positive constant. When $t = 0$, $r = a$ and $\theta = 0$.

(a) Show that P moves on the curve with polar equation:

$$r = \frac{2a}{1 + \cos \theta}$$

(b) Show that the acceleration of P

(i) is constant in magnitude

(ii) has direction parallel to the initial line. [L]

35 A particle P is projected from a point O at an angle of elevation θ, where $0 < \theta < \frac{\pi}{2}$. The initial speed of P is $20 \cos \left(\frac{\theta}{2}\right) \text{ m s}^{-1}$ and the particle moves freely under gravity.

(a) Find in radians to 2 decimal places the value of θ for which the horizontal range of P is greatest, justifying your answer.

(b) Calculate, to the nearest metre, this greatest range. [L]

36 A hollow right circular cone C, with vertex downwards, has its axis vertical and its vertex V fixed on a horizontal plane. The semi-vertical angle of C is $\left(\frac{1}{2}\pi - \beta\right)$, where β is acute. A particle P is projected from V with speed 7 m s^{-1} at an angle of elevation α, where $\alpha > \beta$. C is open-ended and sufficiently deep so that, for all values of α, P hits the curved surface of C.

(a) Show that P hits C after a time of flight of:

$$\frac{10 \sin(\alpha - \beta)}{7 \cos \beta} \text{ seconds}$$

The angle of elevation α can be set to any value greater than β. The largest horizontal circle on the inner surface of C that P can hit has radius R m and is at a vertical height H m above V.

(b) Find R in terms of β.

(c) Find H in terms of R. [L]

37 A right circular cone is fixed with its base horizontal and vertex uppermost. The cone has base radius r and height r. A particle P is projected from the vertex with speed V at an angle of elevation θ. The particle moves freely under gravity and passes through a point on the circumference of the base of the cone. Show that:

$$V^2 = \frac{gr}{1 + \cos 2\theta + \sin 2\theta}$$

Given that V and θ may vary, find

(a) the value of θ for which V^2 is least

(b) the least value of V^2, giving your answer in terms of g and r.

If the cone were replaced by a solid hemisphere, of radius r, and P is projected from the top point of the hemisphere with velocity whose direction and magnitude are identical to those found in (a) and (b), explain why P first strikes the surface of the hemisphere at a point above its horizontal base. [L]

38

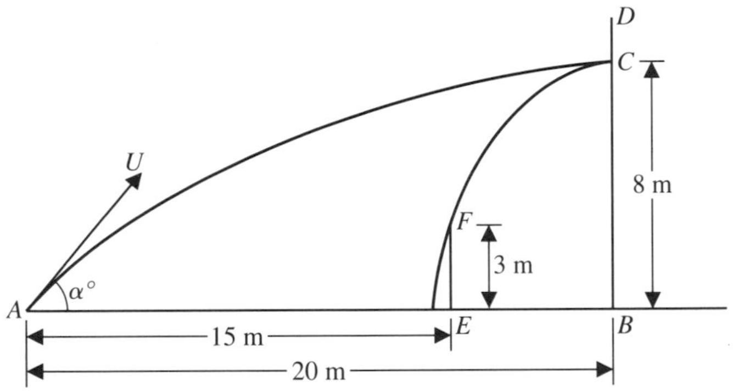

The figure shows the trajectory of a particle projected from a point A on horizontal ground with speed $U\,\mathrm{m\,s^{-1}}$ at an angle of elevation $\alpha°$. The trajectory is in a vertical plane perpendicular to two vertical walls BD and EF standing on the ground at distances 20 m and 15 m respectively from A. The wall EF is of height 3 m. At the instant when the particle reaches its greatest height, it strikes the wall BD at the point C where $BC = 8$ m. Find, correct to 1 decimal place,

(a) the value of α,

(b) the value of U.

On rebounding from the wall BD, the particle just clears the wall EF.

(c) Find the coefficient of restitution between the particle and the wall *BD*.

(d) Calculate the acute angle between the horizontal and the velocity of the particle just as it clears the wall *EF*. [L]

39 A particle is projected from a fixed point *O* with velocity $u\mathbf{i} + \lambda u\mathbf{j}$ and moves with acceleration $-g\mathbf{j}$ where u and λ are positive constants and $\mathbf{i}$ and $\mathbf{j}$ are unit vectors directed horizontally and vertically upwards respectively. At time *t* after leaving *O*, the particle is at the point *P* whose position vector relative to *O* is $x\mathbf{i} + y\mathbf{j}$. Show that

$$y = \lambda x - \tfrac{1}{2}g\frac{x^2}{u^2}$$

Given that $x = a$ when $y = b$ and that $x = 2a$ when $y = 0$, find λ and u^2 in terms of a, b and g.

Find, in terms of a and b, the horizontal displacement of the particle from *O* at the instant when the velocity of the particle is at right angles to the velocity of projection. [L]

40 Points *A* and *B* lie in the same horizontal plane and $AB = d$. The point *C* is vertically above *B* and $BC = h$.

A particle *Q* is thrown vertically upwards from *B* at a speed *u*. When *Q* is at *C*, and is travelling upwards, a particle *P* is projected from *A* with speed *v* at an angle α to the horizontal. The particles collide when *Q* is again at *C*, but travelling downwards.

Show that $\tan \alpha = \dfrac{2u^2 - 3hg}{gd}$. [L]

41 A shell is projected with speed *u* from a point *O* which is at a height *h* vertically above a point *A*. The shell moves freely under gravity and strikes the horizontal plane through *A* at a point *B*. The angle of projection of the shell is chosen so that the distance *AB* is a maximum.

(a) Show that the time of flight *T* is given by

$$g^2 T^2 = 2(u^2 + gh)$$

(b) Find, in terms *u*, g and *h*, the maximum value of the distance *AB*. [L]

42 A particle is projected with speed V from a point O on the top of a cliff of height H above sea level. The particle strikes the sea at a point A which is at a horizontal distance R from O. Show that when R has its greatest value R_0 the angle of elevation β, at which the particle should be projected, satisfies

$$gR_0 \tan \beta = V^2 \qquad \text{[L]}$$

Find R_0 in terms of V, H and g.

43 A particle is projected with velocity V and elevation α from a point O. Show that the equation of the path of the particle, referred to horizontal and vertical axes Ox and Oy respectively in the plane of the path, is

$$y = x \tan \alpha - gx^2(1 + \tan^2 \alpha)/(2V^2)$$

A particle P is projected with velocity $70 \, \text{m s}^{-1}$ from the top of a vertical tower, of height $40 \, \text{m}$, standing on a horizontal plane. The particle strikes the plane at a distance $200 \, \text{m}$ from the foot of the tower. Find the two possible angles of projection. If these angles are α_1, α_2, where $\alpha_1 > \alpha_2$, calculate

(a) the greatest height, correct to the nearest metre, above the top of the tower when P is projected at inclination α_1

(b) the time of flight, correct to the nearest tenth of a second, when P is projected at inclination α_2. [L]

General motion of a rigid body

4

When a rigid body can move freely, its motion can involve both translational and rotational motion. In order to study the motion of a freely moving rigid body, some basic results must first be established.

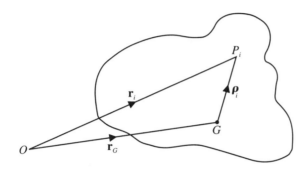

Let O be a fixed origin and let $\mathbf{r}_G$ be the position vector of G, the centre of mass of the body, relative to O. Let P_i be a typical particle of the body and let P_i have mass m_i and position vector $\mathbf{r}_i$ relative to O. Then:

$$\mathbf{r}_i = \mathbf{r}_G + \boldsymbol{\rho}_i \tag{1}$$

where $\overrightarrow{GP_i} = \boldsymbol{\rho}_i$ is the position vector of P_i relative to G.

Then, by definition, summing over all the particles of the body,

$$\sum_i m_i \boldsymbol{\rho}_i = \mathbf{0}$$

And so: $\qquad \displaystyle\sum_i m_i \dot{\boldsymbol{\rho}}_i = \mathbf{0} \quad \text{and} \quad \sum_i m_i \ddot{\boldsymbol{\rho}}_i = \mathbf{0} \tag{2}$

4.1 Kinetic energy

Consider the kinetic energy of the rigid body.

Differentiating equation (1) above gives:

$$\dot{\mathbf{r}}_i = \dot{\mathbf{r}}_G + \dot{\boldsymbol{\rho}}_i$$

And so:
$$\text{K.E.} = \tfrac{1}{2} \sum_i m_i \dot{\mathbf{r}}_i^{\;2}$$

$$= \tfrac{1}{2} \sum_i m_i (\dot{\mathbf{r}}_G + \dot{\boldsymbol{\rho}}_i)^2$$

$$= \tfrac{1}{2} \sum_i m_i \dot{\mathbf{r}}_G^{\;2} + \sum_i m_i \dot{\mathbf{r}}_G \cdot \dot{\boldsymbol{\rho}}_i + \tfrac{1}{2} \sum_i m_i \dot{\boldsymbol{\rho}}_i^{\;2}$$

$$= \tfrac{1}{2} \left(\sum_i m_i \right) \dot{\mathbf{r}}_G^{\;2} + \dot{\mathbf{r}}_G \cdot \sum_i m_i \dot{\boldsymbol{\rho}}_i + \tfrac{1}{2} \sum_i m_i \dot{\boldsymbol{\rho}}_i^{\;2}$$

By the equations (2) above $\dot{\mathbf{r}}_G \cdot \sum_i m_i \dot{\boldsymbol{\rho}}_i = 0$ and since $\sum_i m_i = M$, the mass of the body, then:

$$\text{K.E.} = \tfrac{1}{2} M \dot{\mathbf{r}}_G^{\;2} + \tfrac{1}{2} \sum_i m_i \dot{\boldsymbol{\rho}}_i^{\;2} \tag{3}$$

Now $\tfrac{1}{2} \sum_i m_i \dot{\boldsymbol{\rho}}_i^{\;2}$ has the form of the usual expression for the kinetic energy but with $\dot{\boldsymbol{\rho}}_i$ replacing $\dot{\mathbf{r}}_i$; that is, the velocity relative to G replacing the true velocity. This term is called the **kinetic energy relative to G**.

■ **The kinetic energy (T) of a rigid body, of total mass M, is equal to the sum of the kinetic energy of a particle of mass M moving with G (T_G) and the kinetic energy of the system relative to G.**

$$T = T_G + T \text{ (relative to } G\text{)}$$

If the motion of the rigid body is restricted to a fixed plane then

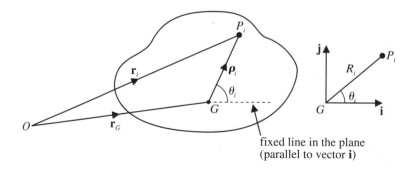

fixed line in the plane
(parallel to vector **i**)

equation (3) above takes a special form.

Let **i** and **j** be unit vectors in the fixed plane, and let $|\boldsymbol{\rho}_i| = R_i$ so that:

$$\boldsymbol{\rho}_i = R_i \cos \theta_i \mathbf{i} + R_i \sin \theta_i \mathbf{j}$$

Since the body is rigid, R_i is constant and so differentiating with respect to time gives:

$$\dot{\boldsymbol{\rho}}_i = (- R_i \sin \theta_i \mathbf{i} + R_i \cos \theta_i \mathbf{j}) \dot{\theta}_i$$

Hence:
$$T \text{ (relative to } G) = \tfrac{1}{2} \sum_i m_i \dot{\boldsymbol{\rho}}_i{}^2$$

$$= \tfrac{1}{2} \sum_i m_i R_i{}^2 \dot{\theta}_i{}^2$$

As the body is rigid, $\dot{\theta}_i = \omega$ for all particles P_i.

So:
$$T \text{ (relative to } G) = \tfrac{1}{2} \omega^2 \left(\sum_i m_i R_i{}^2 \right)$$

$$= \tfrac{1}{2} I_G \omega^2$$

where I_G is the moment of inertia of the body about the axis through G perpendicular to the plane of the motion.

■ **For a rigid body moving in a fixed plane**

$$\text{K.E.} = \tfrac{1}{2} M v_G{}^2 + \tfrac{1}{2} I_G \omega^2$$

4.2 Linear momentum

The linear momentum $\mathbf{p}$ of the rigid body is the vector sum of the momenta of the individual particles of the body. Thus:

$$\mathbf{p} = \sum_i m_i \dot{\mathbf{r}}_i$$

$$= \sum_i m_i \left(\dot{\mathbf{r}}_G + \dot{\boldsymbol{\rho}}_i \right)$$

$$= \left(\sum_i m_i \right) \dot{\mathbf{r}}_G + \sum_i m_i \dot{\boldsymbol{\rho}}_i$$

Equations (2) above showed that $\sum_i m_i \dot{\boldsymbol{\rho}}_i = \mathbf{0}$, so:

$$\mathbf{p} = M \dot{\mathbf{r}}_G = M \mathbf{v}_G \qquad (4)$$

■ **The linear momentum of a rigid body is identical to the momentum of a particle of mass M moving with G.**

4.3 Angular momentum (or moment of momentum)

The angular momentum $\mathbf{h}(O)$ of the rigid body about O is the vector sum of the angular momenta of the individual particles about O.

The (linear) momentum of a typical particle P_i is $m_i\dot{\mathbf{r}}_i$. The moment of momentum of P_i about O is found in the same way as the moment of a force (chapter 1 section 3), that is, using the vector product.

So: moment of momentum of $P_i = \mathbf{r}_i \times (m_i\dot{\mathbf{r}}_i)$

Adding the angular momenta of all the particles of the body gives:

$$\mathbf{h}(O) = \sum_i \mathbf{r}_i \times (m_i\dot{\mathbf{r}}_i)$$

$$= \sum_i m_i(\mathbf{r}_G + \boldsymbol{\rho}_i) \times (\dot{\mathbf{r}}_G + \dot{\boldsymbol{\rho}}_i)$$

by equation (1)

$$= \sum_i m_i\mathbf{r}_G \times \dot{\mathbf{r}}_G + \sum_i m_i\mathbf{r}_G \times \dot{\boldsymbol{\rho}}_i + \sum_i m_i\boldsymbol{\rho}_i \times \dot{\mathbf{r}}_G + \sum_i m_i\boldsymbol{\rho}_i \times \dot{\boldsymbol{\rho}}_i$$

$$= \mathbf{r}_G \times \dot{\mathbf{r}}_G \left(\sum_i m_i\right) + \mathbf{r}_G \times \left(\sum_i m_i\dot{\boldsymbol{\rho}}_i\right) + \left(\sum_i m_i\boldsymbol{\rho}_i\right) \times \dot{\mathbf{r}}_G$$

$$+ \sum_i m_i\boldsymbol{\rho}_i \times \dot{\boldsymbol{\rho}}_i$$

By equations (1) and (2) above, $\displaystyle\sum_i m_i\boldsymbol{\rho}_i = \mathbf{0}$ and $\displaystyle\sum_i m_i\dot{\boldsymbol{\rho}}_i = \mathbf{0}$. Therefore:

$$\mathbf{h}(O) = \mathbf{r}_G \times M\mathbf{v}_G + \sum_i \boldsymbol{\rho}_i \times m_i\dot{\boldsymbol{\rho}}_i \qquad (5)$$

Or:

$$\mathbf{h}(O) = \mathbf{r}_G \times M\mathbf{v}_G + \mathbf{h}_r(G)$$

- **The angular momentum of a rigid body about any point O is equal to the vector sum of the angular momentum about O of a particle of mass M moving with G and the angular momentum of the body relative to G.**

Equations (3) and (5) illustrate the principle of **independence of translation and rotation**.

4.4 Equation of linear motion

Suppose the particle P_i of the rigid body is subject to a force $\mathbf{F}_i$ from external causes, and suppose also that the internal forces are in equilibrium. The equation of motion of P_i is

$$m_i\ddot{\mathbf{r}}_i = \mathbf{F}_i \qquad (6)$$

Adding these equations for every particle of the rigid body gives:

$$\sum_i m_i \ddot{\mathbf{r}}_i = \sum_i \mathbf{F}_i = \mathbf{F}$$

Using equation (1) gives:

$$\sum_i m_i \ddot{\mathbf{r}}_i = \sum_i m_i (\ddot{\mathbf{r}}_G + \ddot{\boldsymbol{\rho}}_i)$$

$$= \left(\sum_i m_i \right) \ddot{\mathbf{r}}_G + \sum_i m_i \ddot{\boldsymbol{\rho}}_i$$

and as, by equations (2), $\sum_i m_i \ddot{\boldsymbol{\rho}}_i = \mathbf{0}$, then:

$$\sum_i m_i \ddot{\mathbf{r}}_i = M\ddot{\mathbf{r}}_G$$

Hence:
$$M\ddot{\mathbf{r}}_G = \mathbf{F}$$

and since, from equation (4):

$$\mathbf{p} = M\dot{\mathbf{r}}_G$$

it follows that:

$$M\ddot{\mathbf{r}}_G = \mathbf{F} = \frac{\mathrm{d}}{\mathrm{d}t}(\mathbf{p}) \tag{7}$$

■ **The centre of mass G of the body has the same acceleration as a particle of mass M situated at G, under the action of a force equal to the resultant of all the external forces acting on the body.**

4.5 Equation of rotational motion

The equation of linear motion for a typical particle of the body (equation (6) above) stated that:

$$m_i \ddot{\mathbf{r}}_i = \mathbf{F}_i$$

and so, taking moments about O for all particles of the body gives:

$$\sum_i \mathbf{r}_i \times m_i \ddot{\mathbf{r}}_i = \sum_i \mathbf{r}_i \times \mathbf{F}_i$$

Using equation (1), $\mathbf{r}_i = \mathbf{r}_G + \boldsymbol{\rho}_i$, gives:

$$\sum_i (\mathbf{r}_G + \boldsymbol{\rho}_i) \times m_i (\ddot{\mathbf{r}}_G + \ddot{\boldsymbol{\rho}}_i) = \sum_i (\mathbf{r}_G + \boldsymbol{\rho}_i) \times \mathbf{F}_i$$

Or:

$$\sum_i \mathbf{r}_G \times m_i \ddot{\mathbf{r}}_G + \sum_i \mathbf{r}_G \times m_i \ddot{\boldsymbol{\rho}}_i + \sum_i \boldsymbol{\rho}_i \times m_i \ddot{\mathbf{r}}_G$$

$$+ \sum_i \boldsymbol{\rho}_i \times m_i \ddot{\boldsymbol{\rho}}_i = \sum_i \mathbf{r}_G \times \mathbf{F}_i + \sum_i \boldsymbol{\rho}_i \times \mathbf{F}_i$$

$$\left(\sum_i m_i\right) \mathbf{r}_G \times \ddot{\mathbf{r}}_G + \mathbf{r}_G \times \left(\sum_i m_i \ddot{\boldsymbol{\rho}}_i\right) + \left(\sum_i m_i \boldsymbol{\rho}_i\right) \times \ddot{\mathbf{r}}_G$$

$$+ \sum_i \boldsymbol{\rho}_i \times m_i \ddot{\boldsymbol{\rho}}_i = \mathbf{r}_G \times \mathbf{F} + \sum_i \boldsymbol{\rho}_i \times \mathbf{F}_i$$

But $\left(\sum_i m_i\right) \mathbf{r}_G \times \ddot{\mathbf{r}}_G = \mathbf{r}_G \times M\ddot{\mathbf{r}}_G = \mathbf{r}_G \times \mathbf{F}$ from equation (7).

Also, by equations (2) $\sum_i m_i \ddot{\boldsymbol{\rho}}_i = \mathbf{0}$ and $\sum_i m_i \boldsymbol{\rho}_i = \mathbf{0}$

Hence:

$$\sum_i \boldsymbol{\rho}_i \times m_i \ddot{\boldsymbol{\rho}}_i = \sum_i \boldsymbol{\rho}_i \times \mathbf{F}_i$$

But:

$$\frac{\mathrm{d}}{\mathrm{d}t}\left[\sum_i \boldsymbol{\rho}_i \times m_i \dot{\boldsymbol{\rho}}\right] = \sum_i \dot{\boldsymbol{\rho}}_i \times m_i \dot{\boldsymbol{\rho}}_i + \sum_i \boldsymbol{\rho}_i \times m_i \ddot{\boldsymbol{\rho}}_i$$

And:

$$\dot{\boldsymbol{\rho}}_i \times m_i \dot{\boldsymbol{\rho}}_i = \mathbf{0}$$

So:

$$\frac{\mathrm{d}}{\mathrm{d}t}\left[\sum_i \boldsymbol{\rho}_i \times m_i \dot{\boldsymbol{\rho}}_i\right] = \sum_i \boldsymbol{\rho}_i \times m_i \ddot{\boldsymbol{\rho}}_i$$

$$= \sum_i \boldsymbol{\rho}_i \times \mathbf{F}_i$$

Or:

$$\frac{\mathrm{d}}{\mathrm{d}t}[\mathbf{h}_r(G)] = \boldsymbol{\Gamma}(G)$$

- **The moment of the external forces about G, $\boldsymbol{\Gamma}(G)$ is equal to the rate of change of $\mathbf{h}_r(G)$, the angular momentum relative to G.**

As was the case with the kinetic energy relationship, when the motion is restricted to a fixed plane the equation takes a special form.

$$\sum_i \boldsymbol{\rho}_i \times m_i \dot{\boldsymbol{\rho}}_i = \sum_i (R_i \cos \theta_i \mathbf{i} + R_i \sin \theta_i \mathbf{j})$$

$$\times (- R_i \sin \theta_i \mathbf{i} + R_i \cos \theta_i \mathbf{j})\dot{\theta}_i$$

$$= \sum_i m_i R_i^2 \dot{\theta}_i \mathbf{k}$$

where **k** is a unit vector perpendicular to the plane of motion.

$$= \left(\sum_i m_i R_i{}^2 \right) \omega \mathbf{k}$$

$$= \mathrm{I}_G \omega \mathbf{k}$$

So:
$$\frac{\mathrm{d}}{\mathrm{d}t}[\mathrm{I}_G \omega] = \Gamma(G)$$

Or:
$$\mathrm{I}_G \dot{\omega} = \Gamma(G)$$

The following examples show the applications of these results.

Example 1

A uniform rod of mass m and length $2a$ is held at an angle β to the vertical with its lower end on a smooth horizontal plane and is then released.

(a) Find the angular speed of the rod just before it strikes the plane.
(b) Find the normal contact force just before it strikes the plane.
(c) Show that the angular acceleration at that instant is independent of β.

As the plane is smooth the only forces acting on the rod are vertical. Hence the horizontal velocity of G, the centre of mass of the rod, remains constant and equal to its original value which was zero.

The centre of mass G therefore moves vertically. Suppose, at time t, G is a distance y above the plane and the rod makes an angle θ with the vertical.

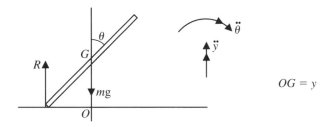

The diagram shows the forces acting on the rod and the directions of the linear and angular accelerations.

$$OG = y = a \cos \theta$$

So:
$$\dot{y} = -a\dot{\theta} \sin \theta$$

$$\ddot{y} = -a\ddot{\theta} \sin \theta - a\dot{\theta}^2 \cos \theta$$

The moment of inertia of the rod about an axis through G perpendicular to the plane of the motion is $\frac{1}{3}ma^2$.

Hence the kinetic energy of the rod is:

$$\text{K.E.} = \tfrac{1}{2}m\dot{y}^2 + \tfrac{1}{2}\left(\frac{ma^2}{3}\right)\dot{\theta}^2$$

$$= \tfrac{1}{2}ma^2\dot{\theta}^2\left(\sin^2\theta + \tfrac{1}{3}\right)$$

The potential energy lost by the rod:

$$\text{P.E.} = mga\cos\beta - mga\cos\theta$$

Since mechanical energy is conserved:

$$\tfrac{1}{2}ma^2\dot{\theta}^2\left(\tfrac{1}{3} + \sin^2\theta\right) = mga(\cos\beta - \cos\theta) \tag{1}$$

(a) When $\theta = \dfrac{\pi}{2}$ this equation becomes:

$$\tfrac{1}{2}ma^2\dot{\theta}_{\frac{\pi}{2}}^2\left(\tfrac{1}{3} + 1\right) = mga\cos\beta$$

So:
$$\dot{\theta}_{\frac{\pi}{2}}^2 = mga\frac{\cos\beta \times 2 \times 3}{4ma^2}$$

$$\dot{\theta}_{\frac{\pi}{2}} = \left(\frac{3g\cos\beta}{2a}\right)^{\frac{1}{2}}$$

So the angular speed of the rod just before it strikes the plane is $\left(\dfrac{3g\cos\beta}{2a}\right)^{\frac{1}{2}}$.

(b) The equation of motion of G vertically gives:

$$\uparrow \qquad m\ddot{y} = R - mg$$

So:
$$R - mg = -ma\left(\ddot{\theta}\sin\theta + \dot{\theta}^2\cos\theta\right) \tag{2}$$

The equation of rotational motion about G gives:

$$\tfrac{1}{3}ma^2\ddot{\theta} = Ra\sin\theta \tag{3}$$

When the rod is about to strike the plane $\theta = \dfrac{\pi}{2}$.

Equation (2) becomes: $R_{\frac{\pi}{2}} - mg = -ma\ddot{\theta}_{\frac{\pi}{2}}$ \hfill (4)

Equation (3) becomes:

$$R_{\frac{\pi}{2}} = \tfrac{1}{3}ma\ddot{\theta}_{\frac{\pi}{2}} \tag{5}$$

Eliminating $\ddot{\theta}_{\frac{\pi}{2}}$ between equations (4) and (5) gives:

$$R_{\frac{\pi}{2}} = \tfrac{1}{4}mg$$

So the normal contact force just before the rod strikes the plane is $\tfrac{1}{4}mg$.

(c) Substituting $R_{\frac{\pi}{2}} = \frac{1}{4}mg$ in equation (5) gives:

$$\ddot{\theta}_{\frac{\pi}{2}} = \frac{3g}{4a}$$

So the angular acceleration just before the rod strikes the plane is independent of β.

(Note that $\ddot{\theta}_{\frac{\pi}{2}}$ can also be obtained by differentiating equation (1) with respect to θ.)

Example 2

A yo-yo is a toy consisting of two circular discs of radius $2a$ and mass m fixed one at each end of a cylindrical axis of radius a and mass $4m$. The line through the axis of the cylinder passes through the centre of each disc. One end of a string is attached to the axle and wound several times round the axle. The yo-yo is held so that the portion of the string which is not in contact with the axle is vertical. The yo-yo is projected vertically downwards with speed $4\sqrt{(ag)}$. Find the speed of the centre of the yo-yo when a length $20a$ of the string has unwound.

Let the velocity and acceleration of G, the centre of mass of the yo-yo, be $\dot{x}$ and $\ddot{x}$ downwards and the angular velocity and angular acceleration of the yo-yo be $\dot{\theta}$ and $\ddot{\theta}$ clockwise.

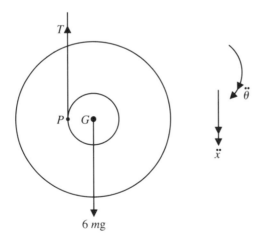

The moment of inertia I_G about the axis through G is:

$$\frac{m}{2}(2a)^2 + \frac{m}{2}(2a)^2 + \frac{4m}{2}a^2 = 6ma^2$$

The point P where the string ceases to have contact with the axle has velocity $\dot{x} - a\dot{\theta}$ vertically downwards. But this point is momentarily at rest, so:

$$\dot{x} = a\dot{\theta} \qquad (1)$$

The linear equation of motion is:

$$6m\ddot{x} = 6mg - T \qquad (2)$$

The equation of rotational motion about G is:

$$6ma^2\ddot{\theta} = Ta \qquad (3)$$

Differentiating equation (1) with respect to time gives:

$$\ddot{x} = a\ddot{\theta}$$

and substituting for $\ddot{\theta}$ in equation (3) gives:

$$6m\ddot{x} = T \qquad (4)$$

Eliminating T between equations (2) and (4) gives:

$$12m\ddot{x} = 6mg$$

So:

$$\ddot{x} = \frac{g}{2}$$

To find the speed use the equation $v^2 = u^2 + 2as$ with $v = 4\sqrt{(ag)}$, $a = \dfrac{g}{2}$ and $s = 20a$ which gives:

$$v^2 = 16ag + 2\frac{g}{2} \times 20a$$

$$v^2 = 36ag$$

$$v = 6\sqrt{(ag)}$$

The speed of the centre of the yo-yo when a length of $20a$ of the string has unwound is $6\sqrt{(ag)}$.

Example 3

A uniform solid cylinder of mass 8 kg and radius 0.25 m has a string attached to a point of its surface and wound several times around the cylinder. The cylinder rests with its curved surface on a rough horizontal plane and the string is pulled in a direction parallel to the plane and perpendicular to the axis of the cylinder as shown in the diagram:

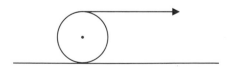

When the tension in the string is 30 N the cylinder rolls along the plane. Determine the minimum value of the coefficient of friction between the cylinder and the plane.

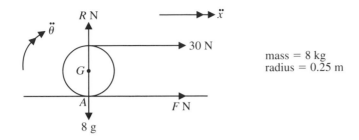

Let the magnitude of the friction force be F N. The friction force acts in the direction opposing the relative motion between the cylinder and the plane.

Let the accelerations of the cylinder be $\ddot{x}$ (linear) and $\ddot{\theta}$ (angular) as shown.

Consider the motion of the point of contact, A. The velocity of A due to the translation is $\dot{x}$ to the right. The velocity of A due to the rotation is $r\dot{\theta} = 0.25\,\dot{\theta}$ to the left.

As the cylinder is not sliding, the velocity of A is zero. So:

$$\dot{x} - 0.25\dot{\theta} = 0$$

Differentiating with respect to time gives:

$$\ddot{x} - 0.25\ddot{\theta} = 0 \qquad (1)$$

This gives a connection between the linear and angular accelerations of the cylinder. This only arises in cases where there is no sliding.

For the linear motion of the cylinder:

$$8\ddot{x} = 30 + F \qquad (2)$$

Consider the rotation of the cylinder about its axis. The moment of inertia of the cylinder about this axis is:

$$\tfrac{1}{2}mr^2 = \left(\tfrac{1}{2} \times 8 \times 0.25^2\right) \text{kg\,m}^2$$
$$= 0.25 \text{ kg\,m}^2$$

The equation of rotational motion, $I\ddot{\theta} = \Gamma(G)$ gives:

$$\circlearrowright \quad 0.25\ddot{\theta} = 30 \times 0.25 - F \times 0.25 \qquad (3)$$

Eliminating $\ddot{x}$ and $\ddot{\theta}$ between equations (1), (2) and (3) gives:

$$\tfrac{1}{8}(30 + F) - (30 \times 0.25 - F \times 0.25) = 0$$
$$30 + F - 60 + 2F = 0$$
$$3F = 30$$
$$F = 10$$

The friction force acting at A has magnitude 10 N.

The cylinder is not moving vertically, so $R = 8g$. As there is no sliding, $F \leqslant \mu R$

So:
$$10 \leqslant \mu \times 8 \times 9.8$$

$$\mu \geqslant \frac{10}{8 \times 9.8}$$

$$\mu \geqslant 0.128$$

The minimum value of the coefficient of friction is 0.128 (to 3 significant figures).

Exercise 4A

1 A hoop of mass m and radius r is rolling along a horizontal plane. The centre of the hoop is moving with constant speed v. Find the kinetic energy of the hoop.

2 A uniform solid sphere of mass $5m$ and radius r is rolling along a horizontal plane. At the moment when the kinetic energy of the sphere is $\frac{2}{7} mgr$ find

(a) the linear speed of the sphere

(b) the angular speed of the sphere.

3 A pole of length 3 m and mass 5 kg is released from rest when at an angle of 85° to a smooth horizontal surface and its lower end is in contact with the surface. Assuming the pole can be modelled as a uniform rod, calculate

(a) the angular speed of the pole just before it strikes the surface

(b) the normal contact force just before the pole strikes the surface.

4 A uniform rod AB of length $2l$ and mass m has a small ring of mass $\frac{1}{2}m$ attached at A. The ring is free to slide on a smooth horizontal wire. The rod is initially held at an angle of 30° to the wire, the rod and the wire being in the same vertical plane, and is then released from rest. Find, in terms of g and θ, the angular speed of the rod when it is at an angle θ with the wire.

5 A uniform rod of mass m and length $2l$ has its lower end resting on a rough horizontal surface. The rod is held at an angle of 30° to the vertical and is then released. Given that the lower end of the rod immediately slips, find the greatest possible value of the coefficient of friction.

6 A uniform rod AB of mass m and length $3l$ is held with end A on a smooth floor and end B against a smooth vertical wall. The vertical plane through the rod is perpendicular to the wall. The rod is released from rest when B is at a height h above the floor. At time t, B is at a height y above the floor and A is at a distance x from the foot of the wall. Show that

$$3l^2\dot{x}^2 = gy^2(h - y)$$

and find the value of y when B leaves the wall.

4.6 Rolling and sliding motion

A case of two-dimensional motion which is of particular interest and occurs frequently is the motion of a rough body of circular cross-section (a sphere, cylinder, disc or hoop) on a rough plane. An example of such a motion is that of a billiard ball moving in a straight line on a billiard table. The ball may be projected with or without an angular velocity about a horizontal axis perpendicular to the plane of motion, depending on how the cue strikes the ball. The friction of the table may increase or decrease the angular speed as the motion proceeds, and in most cases a state is reached when the speed of the centre and the angular velocity are such that the ball is instantaneously rolling. There are interesting questions to be answered as to whether the ball continues to roll or if it slips in a different way. When this type of motion is taking place on an inclined plane, gravity is an additional factor to be taken into account.

When the character of the motion changes from sliding to rolling or vice-versa, in general the frictional force alters discontinuously.

Where there is relative *slipping* of rough surfaces in contact, the frictional force at the point of contact is doing work and so mechanical energy is not conserved. When *rolling* takes place, no work is done by the frictional force and so mechanical energy is conserved.

The main features to be remembered when solving such problems are:

(1) If the body **rolls**, the point of contact between the body and the surface is (instantaneously) at rest. As in example 3 of section 4.5, this allows a relationship between the linear and angular accelerations to be determined.

In this case the frictional force, F, is unknown and must be determined from the equations of motion.

- **The condition for rolling is that the point of contact of the body and the surface has zero velocity.**

(2) If the body **slips**, the condition for rolling is not satisfied but the frictional force, F, takes its limiting value μR. The direction of the frictional force acting on one of the surfaces in contact is opposite to the direction of the motion of that surface relative to the other surface.

(3) The conditions of projection enable the nature of the motion to be determined in its initial stages.

The following examples illustrate the solution of problems involving rolling and sliding motion.

Example 4

A uniform solid cylinder of mass m and radius r is rotating about its axis which is horizontal with angular speed ω. It is gently lowered onto a rough horizontal plane. The coefficient of friction between the cylinder and the plane is μ. Show that sliding will take place for a time $\dfrac{r\omega}{3\mu g}$ and find, in terms of r, ω, μ and g, the distance travelled by the centre of mass during this time.

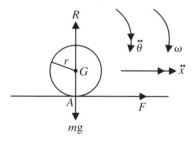

Assuming that ω is clockwise as shown in the diagram, initially the velocity of the point of contact, A, is ωr to the left. So the sphere is sliding and F must act towards the right.

Let the angular acceleration of the cylinder be $\ddot{\theta}$ clockwise and the linear acceleration be $\ddot{x}$ to the right as shown.

Since there is no vertical motion: $R = mg$

Since sliding is taking place: $F = \mu R$

So: $F = \mu mg$ (1)

The linear equation of motion gives:

$$m\ddot{x} = F$$

And so, using equation (1):

$$\ddot{x} = \mu g$$ (2)

The moment of inertia of the cylinder about its axis is $\frac{1}{2}mr^2$, so the equation of rotational motion gives:

$$2 \quad \tfrac{1}{2}mr^2\ddot{\theta} = -Fr$$

Again, using equation (1):

$$\ddot{\theta} = -2\frac{\mu g}{r} \qquad (3)$$

Integrating equation (2) with respect to t gives:

$$\dot{x} = \mu g t \qquad (4)$$

as $\dot{x} = 0$ when $t = 0$.

Integrating equation (3) gives:

$$\dot{\theta} = \omega - 2\frac{\mu g t}{r}$$

as $\dot{\theta} = \omega$ when $t = 0$.

The velocity of A is $\dot{x} - r\dot{\theta}$ to the right. Sliding will take place until $\dot{x} - r\dot{\theta}$ becomes zero. That is, until:

$$\mu g t - r\left(\omega - 2\frac{\mu g t}{r}\right) = 0$$

$$3\mu g t = r\omega$$

$$t = \frac{r\omega}{3\mu g}$$

Hence sliding will take place for a time $\dfrac{r\omega}{3\mu g}$.

To find the distance travelled by the centre of mass during this time, integrate equation (4) with respect to t:

$$x = \tfrac{1}{2}\mu g t^2$$

as $x = 0$ when $t = 0$.

When $t = \dfrac{r\omega}{3\mu g}$, $x = \tfrac{1}{2}\mu g\left(\dfrac{r\omega}{3\mu g}\right)^2 = \dfrac{r^2\omega^2}{18\mu g}$

The cylinder will travel a distance $\dfrac{r^2\omega^2}{18\mu g}$ while sliding.

Example 5

A uniform solid sphere of mass m and radius r is rolling down a line of greatest slope of a plane inclined at an angle α to the horizontal. Given that the coefficient of friction between the sphere and the plane is 0.1, calculate the maximum possible value of α.

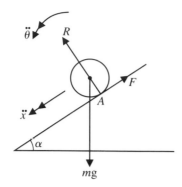

Let the linear acceleration of the centre of mass be $\ddot{x}$ down the plane and the angular acceleration of the sphere be $\ddot{\theta}$ anticlockwise.

The sphere will tend to slip down the plane. So the frictional force F will act up the plane to oppose this. As the sphere is rolling, the instantaneous velocity of the point of contact, A, is zero (condition for rolling).

So:
$$\dot{x} - r\dot{\theta} = 0$$

And differentiating with respect to t gives:
$$\ddot{x} - r\ddot{\theta} = 0 \qquad (1)$$

The linear equation of motion parallel to the plane gives:
$$m\ddot{x} = mg \sin \alpha - F \qquad (2)$$

Now consider the rotational motion of the sphere. The moment of inertia of the sphere about any axis through its centre of mass G is $\frac{2}{5}mr^2$.

The equation of rotational motion gives:
$$\tfrac{2}{5} mr^2 \ddot{\theta} = Fr$$

So:
$$F = \tfrac{2}{5} mr\ddot{\theta} \qquad (3)$$

Eliminating $\ddot{x}$ and $\ddot{\theta}$ between equations (1), (2) and (3) gives:
$$\left(g \sin \alpha - \frac{F}{m} \right) - \frac{5F}{2m} = 0$$

$$2mg \sin \alpha - 2F - 5F = 0$$

$$7F = 2mg \sin \alpha$$

So:
$$F = \frac{2mg}{7} \sin \alpha$$

As the sphere has no acceleration perpendicular to the plane, the equation of motion in this direction gives:
$$0 = R - mg \cos \alpha$$

So:
$$R = mg \cos \alpha$$

But there is no sliding, so: $F \leqslant \mu R$ and as $\mu = 0.1$ this gives:

$$\frac{2mg}{7} \sin \alpha \leqslant 0.1mg \cos \alpha$$

$$\frac{\sin \alpha}{\cos \alpha} \leqslant 0.1 \times \tfrac{7}{2}$$

$$\tan \alpha \leqslant 0.35$$

$$\alpha \leqslant 19.29°$$

The maximum angle of inclination of the plane is 19.3°.

Example 6

A uniform hollow sphere of mass 5 kg and diameter 1 m rolls from rest down a line of greatest slope of a plane which is inclined at an angle of 30° to the horizontal. Calculate

(a) the kinetic energy of the sphere when it has moved a distance 2 m down the plane
(b) the linear speed of the centre of mass at this moment.

[You may assume that the moment of inertia of a hollow sphere about any axis through its centre of mass is $\frac{2}{3} \times$ mass $\times$ radius^2.]

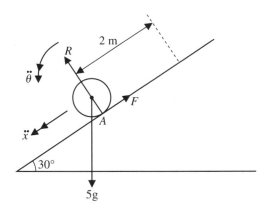

As the sphere starts from rest, it will tend to slide down the plane and so the frictional force, F, will act up the plane.

The normal reaction, R, and frictional force, F, do not move their point of application and so neither force does any work on the sphere.

So, by the work-energy principle, the total mechanical energy of the system is constant.

$$\text{P.E. lost by sphere} = \text{K.E. gained by sphere}$$

(a) $\qquad$ P.E. lost $= mgh = (5 \times 9.8 \times 2 \sin 30)\,\text{J} = 49\,\text{J}$

Hence the kinetic energy of the sphere when it has moved a distance 2 m is 49 J.

(b) K.E. gained by the sphere $= \frac{1}{2}m\dot{x}^2 + \frac{1}{2}I\dot{\theta}^2$

The moment of inertia of the sphere about any axis through its centre of mass $G = \left(\frac{2}{3} \times 5 \times 0.5^2\right)\,\text{kg}\,\text{m}^2$

$$= \tfrac{5}{6}\,\text{kg}\,\text{m}^2$$

So: $\qquad$ K.E. gained $= \frac{1}{2} \times 5\dot{x}^2 + \frac{1}{2} \times \frac{5}{6}\dot{\theta}^2$

Considering the point of contact A, the condition for rolling gives:

$$0.5\dot{\theta} = \dot{x}$$

So, substituting for θ:

$$\text{K.E. gained by sphere} = \tfrac{1}{2} \times 5\dot{x}^2 + \tfrac{1}{2} \times \tfrac{5}{6} \times (2\dot{x})^2$$

$$= \tfrac{5}{2}\dot{x}^2 + \tfrac{5}{3}\dot{x}^2$$

$$= \tfrac{25}{6}\dot{x}^2$$

But from (a), K.E. gained by sphere $= 49\,\text{J}$.

So: $\qquad\qquad\qquad \frac{25}{6}\dot{x}^2 = 49$

$$\dot{x}^2 = 49 \times \tfrac{6}{25}$$

$$\dot{x} = 3.43$$

The linear speed of the centre of mass is $3.43\,\text{ms}^{-1}$ (to 3 significant figures).

Exercise 4B

1 A hollow cylindrical pipe of mass $3m$ and radius r is held at rest on a rough plane inclined at $30°$ to the horizontal. It is released and rolls down a line of greatest slope of the plane. Given that the coefficient of friction between the pipe and the plane is $\frac{1}{4}$, determine whether or not the pipe is sliding.

2 A uniform solid sphere of mass $10m$ and diameter d is rotating about a horizontal axis through its centre with angular speed ω. It is gently lowered onto a rough horizontal plane. The coefficient of friction between the sphere and the plane is μ.

Show that sliding will take place for a time $\dfrac{\omega d}{7\mu g}$ and find the distance travelled by the centre of mass during this time.

3 A uniform solid sphere of mass 0.75 kg and radius 0.2 m is
projected along a rough horizontal table. The sphere is not
spinning initially and the centre of mass is initially moving with
speed $14\,\text{ms}^{-1}$. The sphere slides for the first three seconds of the
motion. Calculate
  (a) the coefficient of friction between the table and the sphere
  (b) the speed of the centre of the sphere three seconds after
      projection
  (c) the work done against friction during the first 3 seconds of
      the motion.

4 A uniform circular disc of mass m and radius a rolls down a line
of greatest slope of a rough plane which is inclined at an angle of
$30°$ to the horizontal. The disc is in a vertical plane throughout
the motion. Find
  (a) the acceleration of the centre of the disc
  (b) the minimum value of the coefficient of friction between the
      disc and the plane
  (c) the distance the disc travels from rest in 2 seconds.

5 A uniform hollow open cylinder of mass $2m$ and radius r rolls
down a line of greatest slope of a plane which is inclined at an
angle of $45°$ to the horizontal. The axis of the cylinder is
horizontal throughout the motion. Given that the cylinder is on
the point of slipping, calculate the coefficient of friction between
the cylinder and the plane.

6 A uniform solid cylinder of mass 6 kg and radius 0.25 m rolls
down a line of greatest slope of a plane which is inclined at an
angle of $20°$ to the horizontal. The axis of the cylinder is
horizontal throughout the motion. Calculate
  (a) the kinetic energy of the cylinder when it has moved 3 m
      from rest
  (b) the angular speed of the cylinder at this moment.

7 A uniform disc of mass $2m$ and radius r is rotating with angular
speed ω in a vertical plane about a horizontal axis through its
centre. The disc is placed on a rough horizontal plane. Given
that the disc slips for a time T, find the coefficient of friction
between the disc and the plane. Find also the distance moved by
the disc before slipping ceases.

8 A uniform solid cylinder of mass m and radius r is projected up a line of greatest slope of a plane inclined at an angle θ to the horizontal. The axis of the cylinder is perpendicular to the line of greatest slope of the plane throughout the motion. Initially the cylinder has no rotational motion and the speed of the centre of mass is u. Show that the cylinder will slip for time t given by:

$$t = \frac{u}{3\mu g \cos \theta + g \sin \theta}$$

where μ is the coefficient of friction between the cylinder and the plane and that the cylinder will continue to move up the plane for a further time:

$$\frac{\mu \cos \theta u}{(3\mu \cos \theta + \sin \theta) g \sin \theta}$$

4.7 The effect of an impulse on a rigid body which is unconstrained

Previously, in Book M1 chapter 5, Book M2 chapter 5 and Book M3 chapter 4, the effect of an impulse on a particle was studied. In Book M3 chapter 2, the effect of an impulse on a rigid body which was free to rotate about a fixed smooth axis was studied. In the former cases the particle moved in a straight line after the impulse was applied; in the latter, the impulse could only cause rotation about the axis. In these cases the model used was either a particle or a rigid body which was free to rotate about a fixed axis. Now the model can be refined to fit the situation where a rigid body which is unconstrained receives an impulse. In this case both rotation and translation are possible.

If $\mathbf{u}_i$ and $\mathbf{v}_i$ are the velocities of the particle P_i immediately before and immediately after the action of an impulse I_i then:

$$m_i \mathbf{v}_i - m_i \mathbf{u}_i = \mathbf{I}_i \tag{1}$$

Adding these equations for every particle of the rigid body gives:

$$\sum_i m_i \mathbf{v}_i - \sum_i m_i \mathbf{u}_i = \sum_i \mathbf{I}_i$$

But $\sum_i m_i \mathbf{v}_i$ is the momentum of the system after the impulse. In section 4.2 it was shown that $\sum_i m_i \mathbf{v}_i = M\mathbf{v}_G$ where $\mathbf{v}_G$ is the velocity of the centre of mass after the impulse and M is the total mass of the body. Similarly, $\sum_i m_i \mathbf{u}_i = M\mathbf{u}_G$ where $\mathbf{u}_G$ is the velocity of the centre of mass before the impulse.

Hence:
$$M\mathbf{v}_G - M\mathbf{u}_G = \sum_i \mathbf{I}_i = \mathbf{J}$$

where $\mathbf{J}$ is the resultant of the external impulses.

- **The change in velocity of G is the same as the change in velocity of a particle of mass M at G under the action of all the external forces transferred to act at G.**

Taking the vector product of equation (1) with $\mathbf{r}_i - \mathbf{r}_A$ where A is an arbitrary point gives:
$$(\mathbf{r}_i - \mathbf{r}_A) \times m_i\mathbf{v}_i - (\mathbf{r}_i - \mathbf{r}_A) \times m_i\mathbf{u}_i = (\mathbf{r}_i - \mathbf{r}_A) \times \mathbf{I}_i$$

(This is sometimes called 'taking moments' about A.)

Adding these equations for every particle of the rigid body gives:
$$\sum_i (\mathbf{r}_i - \mathbf{r}_A) \times m_i\mathbf{v}_i - \sum_i (\mathbf{r}_i - \mathbf{r}_A) \times m_i\mathbf{u}_i = \sum_i (\mathbf{r}_i - \mathbf{r}_A) \times \mathbf{I}_i = \mathbf{K}(A)$$

The left-hand side of this equation is the change in the angular momentum of the rigid body about A and the right-hand side is the moment of the external impulses about A. Thus:

- **The change in angular momentum about any point A is equal to the moment of the external impulses about A.**

Since it has been assumed that no change of position occurs during the action of the impulses, any motion of the point A does not effect the result. In particular, if $\mathbf{K}(A) = \mathbf{0}$, the angular momentum is unaltered.

When the motion is restricted to a plane, the result simplifies to:
$$I_A\Omega_2 - I_A\Omega_1 = K_A$$

where I_A is the moment of inertia of the body about the axis through A perpendicular to the plane of motion, Ω_1 and Ω_2 are the angular velocities of the body before and after the impulse and K_A is the moment of the external impulses about the axis through A.

Example 7
A uniform rod AB of mass m and length $2l$ falls freely from rest in a horizontal position. When the rod has fallen a distance h, the point C of the rod, where $AC = \dfrac{l}{2}$, strikes a fixed smooth horizontal rail.

The rail is perpendicular to the rod and the rod does not rebound on impact. Find:

(a) the angular speed with which the rod begins to turn
(b) the impulse exerted on the rod by the rail at the moment of impact.

(a) When the rod has fallen a distance h, the speed v of its centre of mass G can be obtained from $v^2 = u^2 + 2as$.

So: $$v^2 = 2gh$$

and the speed of G just before impact is $\sqrt{(2gh)}$.

Now draw diagrams of the situations just before and just after impact:

Before impact: After impact:

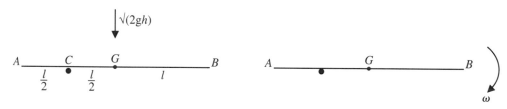

Since the rod does not rebound, just after impact the rod will be rotating about a perpendicular axis L through C.

Let the angular speed of the rod about L be ω. The moment of the impulse about L must be equal to the change in angular momentum of the rod. The rod receives its impulse at C, so the moment of the impulse about L is zero. The moment of momentum about L before impact is the moment of the momentum of a particle of mass m placed at G.

The moment of the momentum about L before impact is $m\sqrt{(2gh)} \times \dfrac{l}{2}$.

Angular momentum about L after impact $= I_L \omega$. Moment of inertia, I_L, of the rod about L:

$$I_L = \tfrac{1}{3}ml^2 + m\left(\frac{l}{2}\right)^2 \quad \text{(by the parallel axis theorem)}$$

$$= \tfrac{1}{3}ml^2 + \tfrac{1}{4}ml^2$$

$$= \tfrac{7}{12}ml^2$$

So the angular momentum after impact $= \tfrac{7}{12}ml^2\omega$

Hence: $$m\sqrt{(2gh)} \times \frac{l}{2} = \tfrac{7}{12}ml^2\omega$$

So:
$$\omega = \frac{12}{7l^2} \times \frac{l}{2} \sqrt{(2gh)}$$
$$\omega = \frac{6}{7l} \sqrt{(2gh)}$$

The rod begins to turn with angular speed $\frac{6}{7l}\sqrt{(2gh)}$.

(b) The impulse received by the rod is equal to the increase in the momentum of a particle of mass m situated at G. The linear velocity of the centre of mass just after impact is $\frac{l}{2}\omega$ downwards.

As the rod is moving downwards in a horizontal position just before striking the rod, the impulse the rod receives is vertically upwards.

For a particle of mass m situated at G:

Momentum before impact $= m\sqrt{(2gh)}$ ↓

Momentum after impact $= m\frac{l}{2}\omega$ ↓

Impulse $=$ gain of momentum

So: Impulse ↑ $= -m\frac{l}{2}\omega + m\sqrt{(2gh)}$
$$= -m\frac{6}{7l}\sqrt{(2gh)} \times \frac{l}{2} + m\sqrt{(2gh)}$$
$$= -\tfrac{3}{7}m\sqrt{(2gh)} + m\sqrt{(2gh)}$$
$$= \tfrac{4}{7}m\sqrt{(2gh)}$$

The impulse exerted on the rod by the rail is $\tfrac{4}{7}m\sqrt{(2gh)}$ upwards.

Example 8

A uniform rod AB of mass m and length $2l$ is lying at rest on a smooth horizontal table. A particle P of mass $3m$ is moving with speed u on the table in a direction perpendicular to the rod when it strikes the rod at the point C where $AC = \frac{l}{2}$. The coefficient of restitution between the rod and the particle is $\frac{1}{3}$. Find

(a) the initial angular speed of the rod
(b) the speed of P after impact.

(a) First draw two diagrams to show the situations just before and just after the impact.

Before impact: After impact: ↑v

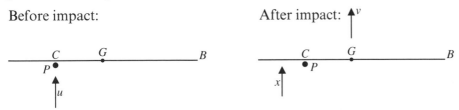

Just after the impact, let the linear speed of G, the centre of mass of the rod, be v and the angular speed of the rod be ω as shown. Let the speed of P after the impact be x.

Here we have a case of two colliding bodies and so the principle of conservation of momentum applies as the impulses on the bodies are equal in magnitude but opposite in direction. To apply this principle, consider the motion of a particle of mass m situated at G.

As the rod is initially at rest,

$$\text{Total initial momentum of system} = \text{initial momentum of } P$$

$$= 3mu$$

$$\text{Total final momentum of system} = \text{final momentum of } P$$
$$+ \text{ momentum of a particle of mass } m \text{ moving with speed } v$$

$$= 3mx + mv$$

So, by the conservation of momentum:

$$3mu = 3mx + mv$$

$$3u = 3x + v \qquad (1)$$

For the rotational motion, consider the angular momentum about the centre of mass, G:

$$\text{Initial angular momentum} = \text{moment of initial momentum of } P$$

$$= 3mu \times \frac{l}{2}$$

$$\text{Final angular momentum} = \text{angular momentum of rod}$$
$$+ \text{ moment of final momentum of } P$$

$$= \tfrac{1}{3}ml^2\omega + 3mx\frac{l}{2}$$

So, by the conservation of angular momentum:

$$\tfrac{3}{2}mul = \tfrac{1}{3}ml^2\omega + \tfrac{3}{2}mxl$$

$$3u = \tfrac{2}{3}l\omega + 3x \qquad (2)$$

This problem involves three unknown quantities x, v and ω. To solve the problem three equations are needed. The third equation is obtained by applying Newton's Law of Restitution to the collision of the particle and the rod.

To do this, first find the speed of C after the impact:

$$\text{speed of } C = v + \tfrac{1}{2}l\omega$$

By Newton's Law of restitution:

$e \times$ speed of approach $=$ speed of separation

$$\tfrac{1}{3}u = v + \tfrac{1}{2}l\omega - x \qquad (3)$$

Eliminating x between equations (1) and (2) gives:

$$v = \tfrac{2}{3}l\omega \qquad (4)$$

Eliminating x between equations (2) and (3) gives:

$$\tfrac{1}{3}u = v + \tfrac{1}{2}l\omega - \left(u - \tfrac{2}{9}l\omega\right)$$

$$\tfrac{1}{3}u = v + \tfrac{1}{2}l\omega - u + \tfrac{2}{9}l\omega$$

$$v = \tfrac{13}{18}l\omega - \tfrac{4}{3}u \qquad (5)$$

Eliminating v between equations (4) and (5) gives:

$$\tfrac{2}{3}l\omega = \tfrac{13}{18}l\omega - \tfrac{4}{3}u$$

$$\tfrac{4}{3}u = \tfrac{1}{18}l\omega$$

$$\omega = \tfrac{4}{3}u \times \frac{18}{l}$$

$$\omega = 24\frac{u}{l}$$

The initial angular speed of the rod is $24\dfrac{u}{l}$.

(b) x is the speed of P after the impact.

Substituting $\omega = 24\dfrac{u}{l}$ in equation (2) gives:

$$3u = \tfrac{2}{3} \times 24u + 3x$$

$$3x = 3u - 16u$$

$$x = -\frac{13u}{3}$$

The speed of P after the impact is $\dfrac{13u}{3}$ (in the opposite direction to that shown in the diagram).

Example 9

A uniform square plate $ABCD$ of mass M and side $2a$ is at rest on a smooth horizontal table. An impulse of magnitude J is applied at the corner A in the direction AB.

   (a) Find the speed of G, the centre of mass, immediately after the impact.
   (b) Find the angular velocity of the plate immediately after the impact.
   (c) Determine the magnitude and direction of the velocity of A immediately after the impact.

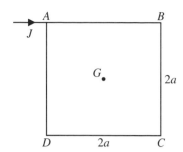

(a) The moment of inertia of the plate about the axis through G perpendicular to the plate can be obtained by using the perpendicular axis theorem:

$$\tfrac{1}{3}Ma^2 + \tfrac{1}{3}Ma^2 = \tfrac{2}{3}Ma^2$$

Let the velocity of G after impact have components u parallel to AD and v parallel to AB, and let the angular velocity of the plate after the impact be ω clockwise.

For the linear motion:

Parallel to AD, there is no impulse.

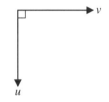

So:
$$Mu = 0$$

Parallel to AB, by the impulse-momentum equation:

$$Mv = J$$

$$v = \frac{J}{M}$$

The speed of G after the impact is $\dfrac{J}{M}$.

(b) Now consider the angular motion about G.

Initial angular momentum $= 0$

 Final angular momentum $= \tfrac{2}{3}Ma^2\omega$ ↻

Moment of impulse $= Ja$ ↻

So:
$$\tfrac{2}{3}Ma^2\omega = Ja$$

$$\omega = \frac{3J}{2Ma}$$

The angular velocity of the plate immediately after the impact is $\dfrac{3J}{2Ma}$ clockwise.

(c) The velocity of A is made up of two parts:

 (i) the velocity v of G parallel to AB

 (ii) the velocity $a\sqrt{2}\omega$ relative to G directed at $45°$ to AB.

But $\omega = \dfrac{3J}{2Ma} = \dfrac{3v}{2a}$

So:
$$a\sqrt{2}\omega = \frac{3v}{2}\sqrt{2}$$

Thus the two parts of the velocity of A are:

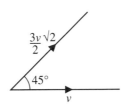

These can be combined to give:

$$v + \frac{3v}{2}\sqrt{2}\frac{1}{\sqrt{2}} = \frac{5v}{2} \qquad \text{parallel to } AB$$

And:
$$\frac{3v}{2}\sqrt{2}\frac{1}{\sqrt{2}} = \frac{3v}{2} \qquad \text{perpendicular to } AB$$

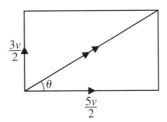

Thus the magnitude of the velocity of A

$$= \sqrt{\left(\frac{9v^2}{4} + \frac{25v^2}{4}\right)} = \frac{v}{2}\sqrt{34}$$

and the direction is at an angle θ to AB where

$$\tan\theta = \frac{3v}{2} \div \frac{5v}{2} = \frac{3}{5}$$

$$\theta = 31.0°$$

Example 10

A wheel in the form of a uniform disc of mass M and radius r is rolling along horizontal ground with speed v when it encounters a step of height $\frac{1}{2}r$ set at right angles to its path. The step is rough enough to prevent slipping and is inelastic. The wheel mounts the step. Show that

$$v^2 \geqslant \tfrac{6}{25} gr$$

Let the angular velocity of the wheel before it strikes the step be ω clockwise.

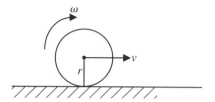

Since the disc is rolling before it strikes the step, the point of contact with the ground has zero velocity. Hence:

$$v - \omega r = 0$$

$$\omega = \frac{v}{r}$$

When the disc strikes the step the only blow is from the step itself and this acts at P.

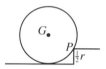

So the angular momentum about P will be conserved. The angular momentum before the impact consists of two parts:

(i) the moment of a momentum vector Mv located at G which is $Mv \cdot \left(\tfrac{1}{2} r\right)$

(ii) the angular momentum relative to G which is $I_G \omega$, where:

$$I_G \omega = \tfrac{1}{2} M r^2 \left(\frac{v}{r}\right) = \tfrac{1}{2} Mvr$$

So: Total angular momentum before impact

$$= \tfrac{1}{2} Mvr + \tfrac{1}{2} Mvr$$

$$= Mvr$$

The angular momentum after the impact is that of a wheel rotating about the fixed point P which is $I_p \Omega$ where:

$$I_p = \tfrac{1}{2} M r^2 + M r^2 = \tfrac{3}{2} M r^2$$

by the parallel axis theorem.

As angular momentum is conserved about P:

$$Mvr = \tfrac{3}{2}Mr^2\Omega$$

So:

$$\Omega = \tfrac{2}{3}\frac{v}{r}$$

For the wheel to mount the step it must turn about P until G is directly above P. The gain in potential energy needed for G to rise a distance $\tfrac{1}{2}r$ is $Mg\tfrac{1}{2}r$.

Just after impact, the kinetic energy of the wheel is given by:

$$\tfrac{1}{2}I_P\Omega^2 = \tfrac{1}{2}\left(\tfrac{3}{2}Mr^2\right)\left(\tfrac{2}{3}\frac{v}{r}\right)^2$$

$$= \frac{Mv^2}{3}$$

This kinetic energy must be greater than or equal to the gain in potential energy required for the wheel to mount the step. Hence:

$$\frac{Mv^2}{3} \geqslant \tfrac{1}{2}Mgr$$

So:

$$v^2 \geqslant \tfrac{3}{2}gr.$$

Example 11

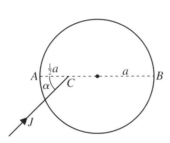

An ice-hockey puck is modelled by a thin uniform disc of mass M and radius a. The puck is lying at rest, flat on a horizontal ice-rink. A horizontal impulse J is applied to the puck, such that the line of action of J is inclined at an acute angle α to the diameter AB of the puck. The line of action of J intersects AB at the point C, where $AC = \tfrac{1}{2}a$ as shown in the diagram.

(a) Find the angular speed of the puck immediately after the impulse has been applied.

(b) Show that the kinetic energy generated by the impulse is

$$\frac{J^2}{4M}(2 + \sin^2 \alpha).$$

[L]

(a) Let the angular speed of the puck immediately after the impulse has been applied be ω.

Using: Change in angular momentum about G = moment of
impulse about G

gives:
$$\tfrac{1}{2} Ma^2 (\omega - 0) = J \sin \alpha \left(\tfrac{1}{2} a \right)$$

So:
$$\omega = J \sin \alpha \cdot \frac{a}{2} \cdot \frac{2}{Ma^2}$$

$$\omega = \frac{J \sin \alpha}{Ma}$$

The angular speed of the puck is $\dfrac{J \sin \alpha}{Ma}$

(b) Now consider the linear motion.

Using: change in momentum of G = impulse

gives: $MV = J$

where V is the speed of G after the impulse parallel to J.

So: $$V = \frac{J}{M}$$

The kinetic energy generated by the impulse is:
$$\tfrac{1}{2} MV^2 + \tfrac{1}{2} I\omega^2$$

$$= \tfrac{1}{2} M \left(\frac{J}{M} \right)^2 + \tfrac{1}{2} \left(\tfrac{1}{2} Ma^2 \right) \left(\frac{J \sin \alpha}{Ma} \right)^2$$

$$= \frac{J^2}{4M} \left(2 + \sin^2 \alpha \right)$$

Exercise 4C

1 A uniform rod AB of mass m and length $2a$ is initially at rest on
a smooth horizontal plane. A particle P of mass m is moving on
the plane with speed v in a direction perpendicular to the rod.

The particle strikes the rod at C where $AC = \dfrac{a}{2}$. The particle

adheres to the rod. Find
   (a) the angular speed with which the rod begins to rotate,
   (b) the loss of kinetic energy of the system due to the impact.
2 A uniform rod AB of mass $3m$ and length $2a$ is initially at rest on
a smooth horizontal plane. A particle P of mass m is moving on
the plane with speed u in a direction at right angles to the rod.

P strikes the rod at *B*. The coefficient of restitution between the rod and the particle is $\frac{1}{3}$. Find

(a) the angular speed with which the rod begins to rotate

(b) the speed of the particle after the impact

(c) the linear speed of the mid-point of the rod.

3 A uniform disc of mass 4*m*, radius *r* and centre *G* is at rest on a smooth horizontal plane. A particle *P* of mass 2*m* is moving on the table with speed *v*. *P* strikes the disc at point *A* on the circumference of the disc when moving in a direction at 120° to *AG*. *P* adheres to the disc. Find

(a) the angular speed with which the disc begins to rotate,

(b) the speed of *P* after the impact.

4 Three identical rods of length 2*l* and mass *m* are joined at their ends to form a triangular framework *ABC*. The framework is initially at rest on a smooth horizontal table. An impulse of magnitude *J* is applied at the mid-point of *AB* in a direction parallel to *BC*. Find

(a) the angular speed with which the framework begins to rotate

(b) the kinetic energy of the system after the impulse.

5 A uniform rod *AB* of mass 3*m* and length 2*l* is lying at rest on a smooth horizontal table. A particle *P* of mass *m* is moving on the table with speed *u*. *P* strikes the rod at point *C* of the rod where $AC = \dfrac{l}{2}$ when moving in a direction at right angles to *AB*. After the impact, *P* continues to move in the same direction but with a speed of $\dfrac{u}{5}$.

(a) Find the coefficient of restitution between *P* and the rod.

(b) Show that $\frac{44}{75}$ of the kinetic energy is lost in the collision.

6 A rectangular lamina *ABCD* with *AB* = 2*a* and *BC* = 2*b* has mass 3*m*. The lamina is falling freely under gravity in a horizontal position when it hits a rough rail which is parallel to *AB* and at a distance *x* from *AB* (*x* < *b*) at the moment of impact. The lamina is moving with speed *u* when it hits the rail and it does not rebound. Find

(a) the initial angular speed of the lamina,

(b) the greatest initial angular speed as *x* varies and the value of *x* for which it occurs.

(c) Given that x takes the value found in (b), find in terms of m and u the magnitude of the impulse exerted by the rail on the lamina at the moment of impact.

7 A wheel of radius r and mass m is rolling along horizontal ground with speed v. The wheel hits the curb which is at right angles to its path and of height $\frac{1}{6}r$. When the wheel touches the curb at P it starts to turn about P without slipping or losing contact. Assuming that the wheel may be modelled as a uniform disc which lies in a vertical plane throughout the motion, find

(a) the angular speed of the wheel as it begins to mount the curb

(b) the least possible value of v which will enable the wheel to mount the curb.

SUMMARY OF KEY POINTS

1 The kinetic energy of a rigid body of mass M is equal to the sum of the kinetic energy of a particle of mass M moving with G and the kinetic energy of the system relative to G. For a rigid body moving in a fixed plane:

$$\text{K.E.} = \tfrac{1}{2}Mv_G^2 + \tfrac{1}{2}I_G\omega^2$$

where v_G is the linear velocity of the centre of mass of the body, ω is its angular velocity about a perpendicular axis through O and I_G is its moment of inertia about that axis.

2 The linear momentum of a rigid body is identical to the momentum of a particle of mass M moving with G.

3 The angular momentum of a rigid body about any point, O, is equal to the vector sum of the angular momentum about O of a particle of mass M moving with G and the angular momentum of the body relative to G.

4 The centre of mass G of a rigid body has the same acceleration as a particle of mass M, situated at G, under the action of a force equal to the resultant of all the external forces acting on the body.

5 The moment of the external forces about G, $\Gamma(G)$ is equal to the rate of change of the angular momentum relative to G.

For a rigid body moving in a fixed plane:

$$I_G \dot{\omega} = \Gamma(G)$$

where $\dot{\omega}$ is the angular acceleration of the body about a perpendicular axis through O, and I_G is the moment of inertia of the body about that axis.

6 When a body is rolling, the point of contact of the body and the surface it is rolling on has zero velocity.

7 When a body is rolling, mechanical energy is conserved.

8 When a body is slipping, the frictional force F takes its limiting value μR.

9 When an impulse is applied to a rigid body, the change in angular momentum about any point A is equal to the moment of the external impulses about A.

Stability

5

5.1 Equilibrium and the potential energy test for stability

In Book M2 chapter 6, it was seen that a rigid body moving in a plane is in equilibrium if:

 (i) the vector sum of the forces acting is zero
 (ii) the algebraic sum of the moments of the forces, about any given point, is zero.

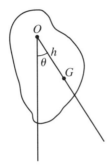

Consider the compound pendulum of mass M, shown in the diagram, which is free to rotate about a smooth horizontal axis through some point O of the body. Let the distance of the centre of mass G from the axis be h. In a general position, OG makes an angle θ with the downward vertical.

There are two positions of equilibrium:

(a) with G vertically below O,   (b) with G vertically above O.

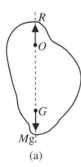

(a)

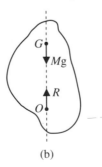

(b)

In both cases all the forces acting on the body are vertical and act through the axis at O.

However it is clear that there is a distinct difference between these two cases. In case (a), if the pendulum is slightly disturbed from this position it will oscillate about its equilibrium position. In case (b), if the pendulum is slightly disturbed it will move right away from its position of equilibrium.

Case (a) is a case of **stable equilibrium** and case (b) is a case of **unstable equilibrium**.

■ **A position of equilibrium for any system is said to be stable when an arbitrary small disturbance does not cause the system to depart from the position of equilibrium. Otherwise it is unstable.**

Relative to the fixed level through O, the potential energy of the compound pendulum, in the general position shown earlier, is:

$$V = -Mgh \cos \theta$$

Then:
$$\frac{dV}{d\theta} = Mgh \sin \theta$$

And:
$$\frac{d^2 V}{d\theta^2} = Mgh \cos \theta$$

Hence V has stationary values when $\dfrac{dV}{d\theta} = 0$, that is when $\sin \theta = 0$.

So $\theta = 0$ and $\theta = \pi$ give stationary values for V. Further when $\theta = 0$, $\dfrac{d^2 V}{d\theta^2} = Mgh$, which is greater than zero, and so V has a minimum for this value of θ.

When $\theta = \pi$, $\dfrac{d^2 V}{d\theta^2} = -Mgh$, which is negative, and so V has a maximum for this value of θ.

The graph of V against θ shows all these properties of V clearly.

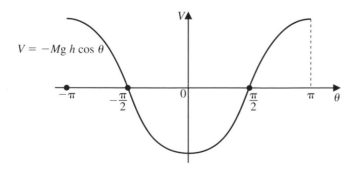

- *V* is a **minimum** at the position of **stable equilibrium**
  V is a **maximum** at the position of **unstable equilibrium**.

As a further illustration consider a bead moving on a smooth wire which is fixed in a vertical plane as shown in the diagram.

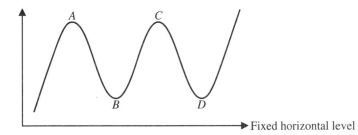

The only points at which the bead can rest in equilibrium are the points *A*, *B*, *C* and *D* where the reaction due to the wire is vertical. Since the potential energy of the bead is directly proportional to the height of the particle above a fixed horizontal level, these equilibrium positions coincide with the positions where *V* is stationary. So:
V is a **maximum** at *A* and *C*, which are **unstable** positions of equilibrium.
V is a **minimum** at *B* and *D*, which are **stable** positions of equilibrium.

These two examples illustrate the following general results:

- **The energy condition for equilibrium**
  In a mechanical system which is free to move, and to whose motion the conservation of energy can be applied, possible positions of equilibrium occur where the potential energy of the system has stationary values.

- **Energy criterion for stability**
  In a mechanical system to which the energy condition for equilibrium applies, minimum values of the potential energy correspond to positions of stable equilibrium and maximum values correspond to positions of unstable equilibrium.

Example 1

A uniform rod *AB*, of mass $12m$ and length $2a$, can turn freely about the end *A* which is smoothly hinged to a vertical wall. A light inextensible string is attached to the other end, *B*, of the rod and passes through a small smooth ring fixed at the point *C*, at a distance $2a$ from *A* and at the same level as *A*. To the other end of the string is attached a particle *P* of mass m. Show that the system is in stable equilibrium when $8 \cos \theta = 1$, where θ is the inclination of *AB* to the horizontal.

The information given is shown in the diagram.

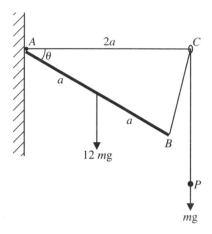

The potential energy of the rod, taking AC as the zero level, is $-12mg\,a\sin\theta$. The potential energy of the particle P is $-mg\,PC$.

Let the length of the string BP be l.

Then: $$PC = l - BC$$

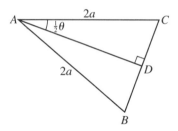

The triangle ABC is isosceles since $AC = AB = 2a$. Therefore, if D is the mid-point of BC, then:

$$\angle ADC = \frac{\pi}{2}$$

And: $$\angle DAC = \frac{\theta}{2}$$

From triangle ADC: $$CD = 2a\sin\frac{\theta}{2}$$

So: $$BC = 2CD = 4a\sin\frac{\theta}{2}$$

The potential energy of the particle P is $-mg\left(l - 4a\sin\frac{\theta}{2}\right)$

So the total potential energy of the system is:

$$V = -12mga\sin\theta + 4mga\sin\frac{\theta}{2} - mgl$$

So: $\dfrac{\mathrm{d}V}{\mathrm{d}\theta} = -12mga \cos\theta + 4mg\,a\left(\dfrac{1}{2}\cos\dfrac{\theta}{2}\right)$

$$= -12mga \cos\theta + 2mg\,a\cos\dfrac{\theta}{2} \qquad (1)$$

For stationary values $\dfrac{\mathrm{d}V}{\mathrm{d}\theta} = 0$

So: $\qquad -12\cos\theta + 2\cos\dfrac{\theta}{2} = 0$

Defining $c = \cos\dfrac{\theta}{2}$, and using $\cos\theta = 2\cos^2\left(\dfrac{\theta}{2}\right) - 1$, gives:

$$-12(2c^2 - 1) + 2c = 0$$

Or: $\qquad -2(12c^2 - c - 6) = 0$

But: $\qquad 12c^2 - c - 6 = (4c - 3)(3c + 2)$

So: $\dfrac{\mathrm{d}V}{\mathrm{d}\theta} = 0$ when $c = \dfrac{3}{4}$ and $c = -\dfrac{2}{3}$.

When $c = \dfrac{3}{4}$ then:

$$\cos\theta = 2\left(\dfrac{3}{4}\right)^2 - 1$$

$$= 2\left(\dfrac{9}{16}\right) - 1 = \dfrac{1}{8}$$

Differentiating equation (1) gives:

$$\dfrac{\mathrm{d}^2V}{\mathrm{d}\theta^2} = 12\,mga \sin\theta + 2mga\left(-\dfrac{1}{2}\sin\dfrac{\theta}{2}\right)$$

$$= 24mga \sin\dfrac{\theta}{2}\cos\dfrac{\theta}{2} - mga \sin\dfrac{\theta}{2}$$

If $\cos\dfrac{\theta}{2} = \dfrac{3}{4}$ then by Pythagoras theorem:

$$\sin^2\dfrac{\theta}{2} = 1 - \cos^2\dfrac{\theta}{2} = 1 - \dfrac{9}{16} = \dfrac{7}{16}$$

So: $\qquad \sin\dfrac{\theta}{2} = \dfrac{\sqrt{7}}{4}$

Hence when $\cos\theta = \dfrac{1}{8}$

$$\dfrac{\mathrm{d}^2V}{\mathrm{d}\theta^2} = 24\,mga\left(\dfrac{\sqrt{7}}{4}\right)\left(\dfrac{3}{4}\right) - mga\left(\dfrac{\sqrt{7}}{4}\right)$$

$$= mga\,\dfrac{17}{4}\sqrt{7} - mga\,\dfrac{\sqrt{7}}{4}$$

$$= mga\,\dfrac{18}{4}\sqrt{7}$$

Since $\dfrac{\mathrm{d}^2V}{\mathrm{d}\theta^2}$ is greater than zero, this position of equilibrium is stable.

Example 2

A particle P, of mass m, is attached to one end of an elastic string of natural length l and modulus of elasticity λ. The other end of the string is attached to a fixed point O. Obtain the potential energy V of the system, when the extension of the string is x. Hence obtain the value of x when the system is in equilibrium and draw a sketch of V against x.

The potential energy of the particle P is $-mg(l + x)$, taking O as the level of zero.

The elastic potential energy of the string is $\dfrac{\lambda x^2}{2l}$. (See Book M2 chapter 4)

Hence the total potential energy is:

$$V = \frac{\lambda x^2}{2l} - mgx + \text{constant}$$

The system is in equilibrium when $\dfrac{\mathrm{d}V}{\mathrm{d}x} = 0$.

That is:

$$\frac{\lambda}{2l}\,(2x) - mg = 0$$

Or:

$$x = \frac{mgl}{\lambda}$$

As $\dfrac{\mathrm{d}^2 V}{\mathrm{d}x^2} = \dfrac{\lambda}{l}$, which is greater than zero, then V is a minimum.

The graph of V against x is:

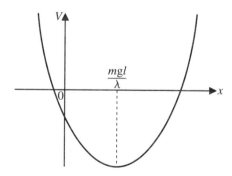

Example 3

A smooth ring P, of mass m, is free to slide on a smooth fixed vertical circular wire of radius a and centre O. A light elastic string of natural length $2a$ and modulus kmg passes through the ring, its ends being fixed to points A and B which are the ends of the horizontal diameter of the wire. Show that, when OP makes an angle 2θ with AB, the ring being below AB, the potential energy of the system is given by:

$$V = kmga\,(\sin\theta + \cos\theta - 1)^2 - mga\sin\theta + \text{constant}$$

Show that if $k > 2 + \sqrt{2}$, the ring is in unstable equilibrium when at the lowest point of the wire.

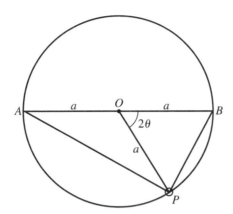

As in Example 1, the triangle OBP is isosceles with $OB = OP$ and therefore the length of BP is $2a\sin\theta$.

Similarly, since the angle $AOP = \pi - 2\theta$ then:

$$\text{length of } AP = 2a\sin\left(\frac{\pi}{2} - \theta\right) = 2a\cos\theta$$

Hence the total length of the elastic string in this position is:

$$AP + PB = 2a\cos\theta + 2a\sin\theta$$

The elastic potential energy of the string is then:

$$\text{P.E.} = \frac{kmg}{2(2a)}[2a\cos\theta + 2a\sin\theta - 2a]^2$$

The potential energy of the particle P, taking **AB** as the zero level, is:

$$\text{P.E.} = -mga\sin 2\theta$$

So the total potential energy of the system is:

$$V = kmga\,(\sin\theta + \cos\theta - 1)^2 - mga\sin 2\theta + \text{constant}$$

The positions of equilibrium are given by $\dfrac{dV}{d\theta} = 0$, that is:

$$\frac{dV}{d\theta} = 2kmga\,(\sin\theta + \cos\theta - 1)\,(\cos\theta - \sin\theta) - mga\,2\cos 2\theta = 0$$

Since $\cos 2\theta = \cos^2\theta - \sin^2\theta$ this gives:

$$\frac{dV}{d\theta} = 2mga\,(\cos\theta - \sin\theta)\,[(k-1)(\sin\theta + \cos\theta) - k] = 0$$

One solution of this equation is given by:

$$\cos \theta = \sin \theta$$

Or:
$$\tan \theta = 1$$

$\Rightarrow$
$$\theta = \frac{\pi}{4}$$

In this case the ring is at the lowest point as $2\theta = \frac{\pi}{2}$.

To investigate the nature of this position, $\dfrac{d^2 V}{d\theta^2}$ is required:

$$\frac{d^2 V}{d\theta^2} = 2mga\{(\cos \theta - \sin \theta)(k - 1)(\cos \theta - \sin \theta)$$
$$+ [(k - 1)(\sin \theta + \cos \theta) - k](-\sin \theta - \cos \theta)\}$$

Substituting $\theta = \dfrac{\pi}{4}$ gives:

$$\frac{d^2 V}{d\theta^2} = 2mga\left[(k - 1)\left(\frac{1}{\sqrt{2}} + \frac{1}{\sqrt{2}}\right) - k\right]\left(-\frac{1}{\sqrt{2}} - \frac{1}{\sqrt{2}}\right)$$

$$= 2mga\left[-2(k - 1) + \frac{2k}{\sqrt{2}}\right]$$

$$= 2mga\left[2k\left(\frac{1}{\sqrt{2}} - 1\right) + 2\right]$$

This position of equilibrium is unstable if $\dfrac{d^2 V}{d\theta^2}$ is less than zero, that is if:

$$2k\left(\frac{1}{\sqrt{2}} - 1\right) + 2 < 0$$

or:
$$2k\left(1 - \frac{1}{\sqrt{2}}\right) > 2$$

So:
$$k > \frac{\sqrt{2}}{\sqrt{2} - 1} = \frac{\sqrt{2}(\sqrt{2} + 1)}{(\sqrt{2} + 1)(\sqrt{2} - 1)} = 2 + \sqrt{2}$$

Example 4

A uniform lamina, of mass M, is in the shape of an isosceles triangle ABC with $AB = AC$. The mid-point of BC is D and $AD = 4l$. The lamina can turn freely about the smooth axis BC which is fixed and horizontal. One end of a light elastic string of natural length l and modulus $\dfrac{5Mg}{24}$ is attached to the vertex A of the triangle. The other end of the string is attached to a point P at a height $4l$ vertically above D.

(a) Obtain the potential energy of the system when DA makes an angle 2θ with the upward vertical.

(b) Find the positions of equilibrium and determine their nature.

The diagram shows the plane PAD, the smooth axis BC intersecting this plane in D.

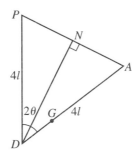

As before, triangle PAD is isosceles with $DP = DA$ and therefore, if N is the mid-point of AP, then $\angle DNA = \dfrac{\pi}{2}$ and $\angle NDA = \theta$.

Hence $NA = 4l \sin \theta$ and $AP = 2NA = 8l \sin \theta$.

The elastic potential energy of the elastic string AP is then:

$$\frac{5Mg}{24} \frac{1}{2l} (8l \sin \theta - l)^2$$

From Book M1 chapter 6, the centre of mass of the triangular lamina is at a distance of $\frac{1}{3} DA$ from D. So $DG = \frac{1}{3} 4l$.

Hence the potential energy of the lamina, taking the level through D as zero, is:

$$Mg \frac{4l}{3} \cos 2\theta$$

So the total potential energy of the system is:

$$V = \frac{4Mgl}{3} \cos 2\theta + \frac{5Mg}{48l} (8l \sin \theta - l)^2$$

$$= \frac{4Mgl}{3} \left(1 - 2 \sin^2 \theta\right) + \frac{5Mg}{48l} \left(64l^2 \sin^2 \theta - 16l^2 \sin \theta + l^2\right)$$

$$= -\frac{8Mgl}{3} \sin^2 \theta + \frac{5Mgl}{48} (64 \sin^2 \theta) - \frac{5Mgl}{48} (16 \sin \theta) + \text{constant}$$

$$and = \frac{Mgl}{3} \left(12 \sin^2 \theta - 5 \sin \theta\right) + \text{constant}$$

So:
$$\frac{dV}{d\theta} = \frac{Mgl}{3}(24 \sin\theta\cos\theta - 5\cos\theta)$$

And:
$$\frac{d^2V}{d\theta^2} = \frac{Mgl}{3}(24\cos^2\theta - 24\sin^2\theta + 5\sin\theta)$$

The positions of equilibrium are given by $\dfrac{dV}{d\theta} = 0$.

So:
$$24\sin\theta\cos\theta - 5\cos\theta = 0$$

or:
$$\cos\theta(24\sin\theta - 5) = 0$$

So: (i) $\cos\theta = 0$

or (ii) $24\sin\theta - 5 = 0$
$$\sin\theta = \tfrac{5}{24}$$

(i) $\cos\theta = 0$

$\Rightarrow \quad \theta = \dfrac{\pi}{2}$

In this position, $2\theta = \pi$ and A is vertically below D.

When $\theta = \dfrac{\pi}{2}$,

$$\frac{d^2V}{d\theta^2} = \frac{Mgl}{3}(-24 + 5) = -19\frac{Mgl}{3}$$

which is negative and so this position is **unstable.**

(ii) $\sin\theta = \tfrac{5}{24}$

$\Rightarrow \quad \theta = 0.21 \qquad$ or $\quad \theta = 2.93°$

$\Rightarrow \quad 2\theta = 0.42 \qquad$ or $2\theta = 5.86°$

Then:
$$\frac{d^2V}{d\theta^2} = \frac{Mgl}{3}\left[24(1 - \sin^2\theta) - 24\sin^2\theta + 5\sin\theta\right]$$

$$= \frac{Mgl}{3}(24 - 48\sin^2\theta + 5\sin\theta)$$

$$= \frac{Mgl}{3}\left(24 - \frac{48 \times 25}{24 \times 24} + \frac{5 \times 5}{24}\right) = \frac{551}{72}Mgl$$

So $\dfrac{d^2V}{d\theta^2}$ is greater than zero and these positions are **stable**.

Exercise 5A

1 A uniform rod, of mass m and length $2a$, is smoothly hinged at one end to a fixed point A. The other end of the rod is attached to a light inextensible string which passes over a smooth peg B at

the same level as A and at a distance $2a$ from it. A mass $\dfrac{m\sqrt{3}}{6}$ is attached to the other end of the string.

Express the potential energy V of the system in terms of θ, the angle which the rod makes with the line AB.

Show that there is a position of equilibrium when $\theta = \dfrac{\pi}{3}$, and determine whether this position of equilibrium is stable or unstable.

2 A uniform rod AB, of mass m and length $2a$, is free to rotate in a vertical plane about the end A. A light elastic string, of modulus kmg and natural length a, has one end attached to B and the other end to a fixed point O which is vertically above A with $OA = 2a$. Show that when AB makes an angle θ with the downward vertical, the potential energy V of the system, when the string is stretched, is given by

$$V = mg\left[(4k - 1)\cos\theta - 4k\cos\left(\frac{\theta}{2}\right)\right] + \text{constant}$$

Deduce that, if $k > \frac{1}{3}$, the equilibrium position in which the rod is vertical, with B below A, is unstable, and that there is an oblique position of equilibrium which is stable.

3 A uniform heavy rod AB, of mass m and length $4a$, can turn in a vertical plane about one end A which is fixed. To the other end B is attached a light elastic string of natural length $3a$ and modulus $\frac{1}{2}mg$. The other end of the string is attached to a light ring which can slide on a smooth horizontal bar which is fixed at a height of $8a$ above A and in the vertical plane through AB. Find the equilibrium positions of the rod and determine their nature.

4 A uniform rod AB, of length $2a$ and mass $2m$, rests with one end A in contact with a smooth vertical wall so that the rod lies in a plane perpendicular to the wall. The rod is supported by a smooth fixed horizontal rail which is parallel to the wall and at a distance c from it. A particle of mass m is attached to the end B of the rod. Show that when the rod makes an angle θ with the upward vertical the potential energy of the system is

$$mg(4a\cos\theta - 3c\cot\theta) + \text{constant}$$

Show also that if $3c > 4a$ there is no equilibrium position, but if

$3c < 4a$ there is one equilibrium position. Determine whether this position is stable or unstable.

5 A bead of mass m can slide on a smooth circular hoop of wire of radius a which is fixed in a vertical position. One end of a light spring, of natural length a and modulus $3mg$, is attached to the bead. The other end of the spring is attached to the highest point of the wire. Show that, when the spring makes an angle θ with the downward vertical, the potential energy V of the system is given by

$$V = \tfrac{3}{2}mga(2\cos\theta - 1)^2 - 2mga\cos^2\theta + \text{constant}$$

Show also that possible equilibrium positions occur when $\theta = 0$ and $\cos\theta = \tfrac{3}{4}$. Determine the nature of these equilibrium positions.

6 Four uniform rods, each of mass m and length $2a$, are smoothly jointed together to form a rhombus $ABCD$. A light elastic string of modulus $2mg$ and natural length a connects A and C. The vertex A is smoothly pinned to a fixed support and the system hangs at rest. Show that there is a position of stable equilibrium in which the angle BCD of the rhombus is $\tfrac{2}{3}\pi$.

5.2 Small oscillations about a position of stable equilibrium

When a system is displaced slightly from a position of stable equilibrium it performs small oscillations about this position. A clock pendulum is an example of such a system.

One of the most convenient ways of obtaining the period of these small oscillations is to derive the approximate equation of motion for the system by differentiating the energy equation.

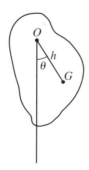

Consider the compound pendulum in the general position shown in the diagram. The potential energy is:

$$V = -Mgh\cos\theta$$

The kinetic energy is $\frac{1}{2}I\dot\theta^2$, where I is the moment of inertia of the body about the horizontal axis through O. The energy equation is therefore:

$$\frac{1}{2}I\dot\theta^2 - Mgh\cos\theta = E \text{ (constant)} \tag{1}$$

Differentiation of this equation with respect to θ gives:

$$I\ddot\theta + Mgh\sin\theta = 0 \tag{2}$$

This equation may also be obtained by differentiating equation (1) with respect to t and cancelling a factor of $\dot\theta$.

Equation (2) may be written as:

$$\ddot\theta + \left(\frac{Mgh}{I}\right)\sin\theta = 0$$

When θ is small $\sin\theta \simeq \theta$ and so:

$$\ddot\theta + \left(\frac{Mgh}{I}\right)\theta = 0$$

This is the equation of a simple harmonic motion (S.H.M.) of period T, where:

$$T = 2\pi\sqrt{\left(\frac{I}{Mgh}\right)}$$

As a further example consider a mass m at the end of an elastic string of natural length l and modulus λ discussed earlier in Example 2.

It was shown that, when the extension is x, the potential energy of the system is:

$$V = \frac{\lambda x^2}{2l} - mg(l+x)$$

The kinetic energy is $\frac{1}{2}m\dot x^2$ and so the equation of energy is:

$$\frac{1}{2}m\dot x^2 + \frac{\lambda x^2}{2l} - mg(l+x) = E \text{ (constant)} \tag{3}$$

Differentiation of equation (3) with respect to x gives:

$$m\ddot x + \frac{\lambda x}{l} - mg = 0$$

or:

$$\ddot x = -\frac{\lambda}{ml}\left(x - \frac{mgl}{\lambda}\right)$$

This is the equation of a simple harmonic motion (S.H.M.) of period $2\pi\sqrt{\left(\dfrac{ml}{\lambda}\right)}$ about a centre of oscillation given by $x = \dfrac{mgl}{\lambda}$, which is the position of equilibrium found earlier.

General theory of small oscillations

In each of the above examples the position of the system was specified by a single parameter. In the first example this was the angle θ and in the second example it was the length x. Such a system, whose position is determined by the value of one variable q, is said to have **one degree of freedom**.

A system whose total mechanical energy remains constant is called a **conservative system** and

$$\text{Kinetic Energy} + \text{Potential Energy} = E \text{ (constant)}$$

For a **conservative system with one degree of freedom**, the kinetic energy is of the form $\frac{1}{2}A(q)\dot{q}^2$ and the energy equation takes the form:

$$\tfrac{1}{2}A(q)\dot{q}^2 + V(q) = E \tag{4}$$

Since the kinetic energy must be positive, $A(q) > 0$ for all possible values of q.

The equation of motion for the system is obtained by differentiating equation (4) with respect to q to give

$$A(q)\ddot{q} + \tfrac{1}{2}A'(q)\dot{q}^2 + V'(q) = 0 \tag{5}$$

The position, or 'motion', given by $q = q_0$, is a possible equilibrium state if $\ddot{q} = \dot{q} = 0$, $q = q_0$ satisfy the equation of motion. Hence $V'(q_0) = 0$ so that V has a stationary value when $q = q_0$.

To obtain the period of small oscillations about this position, substitute $q = q_0 + y$ into equation (5) which gives:

$$A(q_0 + y)\ddot{y} + \tfrac{1}{2}A'(q_0 + y)\dot{y}^2 + V'(q_0 + y) = 0$$

since $\dot{q} = \dot{y}$ and $\ddot{q} = \ddot{y}$.

From the definition of the derivative of f at q_0, we see that for small y:

$$f'(q_0) \simeq \frac{f(q_0 + y) - f(q_0)}{y}$$

or:

$$f(q_0 + y) \simeq f(q_0) + yf'(q_0)$$

Hence:

$$A(q_o + y) \simeq A(q_0) + yA'(q_0)$$
$$A'(q_0 + y) \simeq A'(q_0) + yA''(q_0)$$
$$V'(q_0 + y) \simeq V'(q_0) + yV''(q_0)$$

Assuming y and its derivatives are all small quantities, the equation of motion correct to first order becomes:

$$A(q_0)\ddot{y} + V'(q_0) + yV''(q_0) = 0$$

Since $q = q_0$ is a position of equilibrium $V'(q_0) = 0$ and so the equation of motion to first order is:

$$A(q_0)\ddot{y} + V''(q_0)y = 0$$

or:

$$\ddot{y} + \frac{V''(q_0)}{A(q_0)}y = 0$$

- **If $V''(q_0) > 0$, that is if $q = q_0$ is a position of stable equilibrium, this is the equation of a simple harmonic motion (S.H.M.) of period:**

$$T = 2\pi\sqrt{\left(\frac{A(q_0)}{V''(q_0)}\right)}$$

It is not suggested that this formula should be memorised and quoted. In any given case the approximate equation of motion should be obtained, correct to first order, by differentiating the energy equation. It is often possible, particularly when $q = 0$ is the stable position of equilibrium, to use Maclaurin's series. This is illustrated in the following example where the approximations $\sin x \simeq x$ and $\cos x \simeq 1 - \dfrac{x^2}{2}$ for small x are used.

Example 5

A uniform rod AB, of mass m and length $2a$, can turn freely about the end A which is smoothly hinged to a vertical wall. A light inelastic string of length a and modulus of elasticity mg, connects the end B to the point C which is vertically above A, with $AC = 2a$.

(a) Obtain the positions of equilibrium and determine their nature.
(b) Find the period of small oscillations about the stable position of equilibrium.

The diagram shows the rod in a general position making an angle 2θ with the upward vertical.

(a) The triangle ABC is isosceles with $AB = AC$ and so if M is the mid-point of BC then $\angle AMB = \dfrac{\pi}{2}$ and $\angle BAM = \theta$ so $MB = 2a \sin \theta$ and $BC = 4a \sin \theta$.

The potential energy of the system is:

$$V = mga \cos 2\theta + \frac{mg}{2a}(4a \sin \theta - a)^2$$

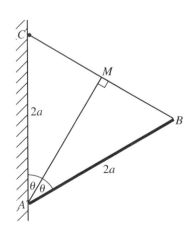

So: $$\frac{\mathrm{d}V}{\mathrm{d}\theta} = mga[-2 \sin 2\theta + (4 \sin \theta - 1) 4 \cos \theta]$$

$$= mga(6 \sin 2\theta - 4 \cos \theta)$$

For positions of equilibrium, $\dfrac{\mathrm{d}V}{\mathrm{d}\theta} = 0$.

So: $$6 \sin 2\theta - 4 \cos \theta = 0$$

or: $$4 \cos \theta[3 \sin \theta - 1] = 0$$

Hence $\cos \theta = 0$ or $\sin \theta = \frac{1}{3}$.

So $\theta = \dfrac{\pi}{2}$ or $\theta = \alpha = \arcsin \frac{1}{3}$.

Now $\dfrac{\mathrm{d}^2 V}{\mathrm{d}\theta^2} = mga(12 \cos 2\theta + 4 \sin \theta)$

(i) When $\theta = \dfrac{\pi}{2}$,

$$\frac{\mathrm{d}^2 V}{\mathrm{d}\theta^2} = mga\left(-12 + \tfrac{4}{3}\right) = -\frac{32mga}{3} < 0$$

and so this position of equilibrium is **unstable**.

(ii) When $\theta = \alpha = \arcsin \frac{1}{3}$,

$$\frac{\mathrm{d}^2 V}{\mathrm{d}\theta^2} = mga[12(1 - 2 \sin^2 \alpha) + 4 \sin \alpha]$$

$$= mga\left[12\left(1 - \tfrac{2}{9}\right) + \tfrac{4}{3}\right] = \tfrac{32}{3} mga > 0$$

and so this position of equilibrium is **stable**.

(b) The moment of inertia of the rod AB about the horizontal axis through A is $\frac{4}{3} ma^2$ and so the kinetic energy of the rod is $\frac{1}{2}\left(\frac{4}{3} ma^2\right)\dot{\theta}^2$ and the energy equation is:

$$\frac{1}{2}\left(\frac{4ma^2}{3}\right)\dot{\theta}^2 + mga \cos 2\theta + \frac{mg}{2a}(4a \sin \theta - a)^2 = E \text{ (constant)}$$

Differentiation with respect to θ gives:

$$\tfrac{4}{3}ma^2\ddot{\theta} - 2mga \sin 2\theta + mga(4 \sin \theta - 1)4 \cos \theta = 0$$

or: $$\tfrac{4}{3}ma^2\ddot{\theta} - 2mga \sin 2\theta + 8mga \sin 2\theta - 4mga \cos \theta = 0$$

Hence the equation of motion is:

$$\tfrac{4}{3}ma^2\ddot{\theta} + 6mga \sin 2\theta - 4mga \cos \theta = 0$$

To find the period of small oscillations about the position of stable equilibrium $\theta = \alpha$, let $\theta = \alpha + y$ where y is small.

Then:

(i) $\sin 2\theta = \sin(2\alpha + 2y) = \sin 2\alpha \cos 2y + \cos 2\alpha \sin 2y$

Using $\cos 2y \simeq 1$ and $\sin 2y \simeq 2y$ gives:

$$\sin 2\theta \simeq \sin 2\alpha \times 1 + \cos 2\alpha \times 2y$$

But: $\qquad \sin 2\alpha = 2 \sin \alpha \cos \alpha$

$$= 2 \times \tfrac{1}{3} \times \sqrt{\left(1 - \tfrac{1}{9}\right)} = \tfrac{2}{3}\sqrt{\left(\tfrac{8}{9}\right)} = \tfrac{4}{9}\sqrt{2}$$

And: $\qquad \cos 2\alpha = 1 - 2 \sin^2 \alpha = 1 - 2 \times \tfrac{1}{9} = \tfrac{7}{9}$

So: $\qquad \sin 2\theta \simeq \tfrac{4}{9}\sqrt{2} + \tfrac{7}{9} \times 2y$

$$\simeq \tfrac{4}{9}\sqrt{2} + \tfrac{14}{9}y$$

(ii) $\cos \theta = \cos(\alpha + y) = \cos \alpha \cos y - \sin \alpha \sin y$

$$\simeq \cos \alpha \times 1 - \sin \alpha \times y$$

$$\simeq \tfrac{2}{3}\sqrt{2} - \tfrac{1}{3}y$$

Using results (i) and (ii) we obtain the approximate equation of motion:

$$\tfrac{4}{3}ma^2\ddot{y} + 6mga\left(\tfrac{4}{9}\sqrt{2} + \tfrac{14}{9}y\right) - 4mga\left(\tfrac{2}{3}\sqrt{2} - \tfrac{1}{3}y\right) = 0$$

or: $$\tfrac{4}{3}ma^2\ddot{y} + mgay\left(\tfrac{6 \times 14}{9} + \tfrac{4}{3}\right) = 0$$

or: $$\tfrac{4}{3}ma^2\ddot{y} + mgay\left(\tfrac{32}{3}\right) = 0$$

So: $$\ddot{y} + \frac{8g}{a}y = 0$$

This is the equation of a simple harmonic motion of period

$$2\pi\sqrt{\left(\frac{a}{8g}\right)}.$$

Exercise 5B

1 A bead P, of mass m, can slide on a smooth wire which is bent into a semicircle of radius a and is fixed with its plane horizontal. Two identical elastic strings of natural length $l(< a\sqrt{2})$ and modulus of elasticity λ, have one end attached to the bead. The other ends are attached to the ends A and B of the wire.

(a) Show that the symmetrical position of the system is stable.

(b) Find the period of small oscillations about this stable position of equilibrium.

2 A uniform rod AB, of mass $2m$ and length $4a$, can turn freely about the end A which is smoothly hinged to a vertical wall. To the other end B is attached a light elastic string of natural length $3a$ and modulus mg. The other end of the string is attached to a light ring which can slide on a smooth horizontal bar which is fixed at a height of $8a$ above A and in a vertical plane through AB. Find the inclination of the rod to the vertical when the system is in stable equilibrium and the period of small oscillations about this position.

3 To the ends A and B of a uniform rod AB are attached two small light rings which can slide on a smooth circular wire of radius b which is fixed in a vertical plane. The rod is of mass m and length $2a$. Obtain the period of small oscillations of the rod about its position of stable equilibrium.

4 Two identical beads, each of mass m, are free to slide on a smooth circular wire of radius a which is fixed in a vertical plane. The beads are at the ends of a light rod of length $2a \sin \alpha$. Show that the period of small oscillations about the stable position of equilibrium is $2\pi \sqrt{\left(\dfrac{a}{g \cos \alpha} \right)}$.

5 A small bead B of mass m can slide on a smooth circular wire of radius a which is fixed in a vertical plane. B is attached to one end of a light elastic string, of natural length $\frac{3}{2}a$ and modulus of elasticity mg. The other end of the string is attached to a fixed point A which is vertically above the centre C of the circular wire with $AC = 3a$.

(a) Show that there is a stable equilibrium position of the system when θ, the angle which the radius through B makes with the downward vertical, satisfies $\cos \theta = -\frac{1}{6}$.

(b) Show that the period of small oscillations about this position is $4\pi \sqrt{\left(\dfrac{27a}{35g} \right)}$.

SUMMARY OF KEY POINTS

1 In a mechanical system which is free to move, and to whose motion the conservation of energy can be applied, possible positions of equilibrium occur when the potential energy of the system has stationary values.

2 In a mechanical system to which the energy condition for equilibrium applies:

- **minimum** values of the potential energy correspond to positions of **stable equilibrium**

- **maximum** values of the potential energy correspond to positions of **unstable equilibrium**.

3 For a conservative system with one degree of freedom for which the energy equation takes the form:

$$\tfrac{1}{2} A(q)\dot{q}^2 + V(q) = E$$

the period of small oscillations about the stable position of equilibrium when $q = q_0$ is:

$$T = 2\pi \sqrt{\left[\frac{A(q_0)}{V''(q_0)}\right]}$$

Review exercise

1 A uniform circular hoop, of mass m and radius r, starts from rest and rolls with its plane vertical and without slipping down a line of greatest slope of a fixed plane which is inclined at an angle α to the horizontal. Prove that the hoop rolls down the plane with constant acceleration $\frac{1}{2}g \sin \alpha$.　　　　　[L]

2 A uniform solid sphere, with centre O, is released from rest on a rough plane inclined at an angle α to the horizontal. The coefficient of friction between the sphere and the plane is μ.
   (a) Given that the sphere rolls without slipping, show that

$$\mu \geqslant \tfrac{2}{7} \tan \alpha$$

   and that O has an acceleration of magnitude $\dfrac{5g \sin \alpha}{7}$ down the plane.
   (b) Given that $\mu < \dfrac{2 \tan \alpha}{7}$ show that the acceleration of O down the plane exceeds

$$\tfrac{5}{7} g \sin \alpha.　　　　　[L]$$

3 A uniform solid sphere is held at rest on a rough plane inclined at an angle α to the horizontal. The sphere is released and rolls without slipping down the plane. Find the acceleration of the centre of the sphere. Find also the least possible value of the coefficient of friction between the sphere and the plane.
   The sphere, which has radius a, is next placed on a rough horizontal table. It is then struck a horizontal blow in a vertical plane containing the centre of the sphere. The line of action of the blow is at a height h above the table. Given that the sphere starts to roll without slipping, show that $5h = 7a$.　　　　　[L]

4 A particle P, of mass $\dfrac{m}{10}$, is fixed to the surface of a uniform solid sphere, of centre O, mass m and radius a. The sphere is placed on a rough horizontal table and initially the system is

held at rest, with OP inclined at $\dfrac{\pi}{3}$ to the upward vertical. The sphere is released and rolls without slipping. Show that, if OP makes an angle θ with the upward vertical at time t after release, the kinetic energy of P is

$$ma^2 \left(\frac{d\theta}{dt}\right)^2 \frac{1 + \cos \theta}{10}$$

Obtain, in terms of m, a, θ and $\dfrac{d\theta}{dt}$, an expression for the kinetic energy of the sphere and hence, or otherwise, show that

$$g(1 - 2 \cos \theta) = 2a\left(\frac{d\theta}{dt}\right)^2 (8 + \cos \theta).$$

Find the speed of O and the speed of P when OP is first horizontal. [L]

5 A uniform solid sphere of radius a is projected down a line of greatest slope of a rough plane inclined at an angle α to the horizontal. Initially the sphere has no angular speed and the velocity of the sphere down the plane is V.

Given that μ, the coefficient of friction between the plane and the sphere, is greater than $\dfrac{2 \tan \alpha}{7}$, show that the sphere will slip for a time

$$\frac{2V}{[g(7\mu \cos \alpha - 2 \sin \alpha)]}.$$

Find, in terms of V, g μ a and α,

(a) the distance through which the centre of the sphere moves while slipping is taking place,

(b) the angular speed at the moment when rolling begins. [L]

6 A uniform hollow circular cylinder has internal radius a and external radius b. The cylinder rolls without slipping down a fixed plane which is inclined at an angle α to the horizontal. The axis of the cylinder always remains perpendicular to the line of greatest slope of the plane. Prove that the centre of the cylinder has constant acceleration of magnitude

$$\frac{2b^2 g \sin \alpha}{a^2 + 3b^2}$$

Hence or otherwise find the corresponding acceleration for a uniform solid cylinder of radius b. [L]

7 A uniform rod AB, of mass m and length $2a$, lies at rest on a smooth horizontal table. A horizontal impulse is applied to the rod at a point P so that, immediately after the impulse, the end A is still stationary. Find the distance AP.

Show that, when the rod is first perpendicular to its initial direction, the centre of mass of the rod has moved a distance $\dfrac{\pi a}{2}$.

[L]

8 A uniform circular disc, of mass m, centre O and radius a, is lying flat on a smooth horizontal table. An impulse, applied to a point P on the rim of the disc, causes P to move with speed v in a direction making an angle θ with PO. Find the velocity of O and the angular speed of the disc after the impulse.

Find also the components of the impulse parallel and perpendicular to PO.

Find also the kinetic energy imparted to the disc by the impulse.

[L]

9 A uniform solid sphere, of mass M and radius a, is rolling, without slipping, along a horizontal plane. The centre of the sphere has speed V. The highest point P of the sphere is suddenly fixed so that the sphere rotates about a horizontal axis through P perpendicular to the original direction of motion.

Show that the magnitude of the impulse at P is $\dfrac{4MV}{7}$.

Show also that the sphere will make complete revolutions about this horizontal axis provided that $9V^2 > 140ga$.

[L]

10 A circular hoop of radius a, is rolling with angular speed $\dfrac{V}{a}$ on a rough horizontal plane. The hoop hits a perfectly rough small peg which is fixed at a height $\frac{1}{5}a$ above the plane, and its point of contact with the peg comes instantaneously to rest. Find the angular speed of the hoop immediately after the impact.

Prove that, if $81V^2 > 80ga$, the hoop loses contact with the peg.

Given that $V = \frac{2}{3}\sqrt{(ag)}$ find the kinetic energy lost as a result of the impact and determine whether or not the hoop will roll over the peg.

[L]

11 A uniform solid sphere, of mass m and radius a, is at rest on a horizontal table. The coefficient of friction between the sphere and the table is μ. The sphere is struck a horizontal blow at a height $1.2a$ above the table. The vertical plane containing the line of action of the blow contains the centre of the sphere. The centre of the sphere starts to move with speed V.

(a) Show that the sphere starts to roll without slipping after a time $\dfrac{V}{7\mu g}$.

When the sphere is rolling without slipping it is struck another horizontal blow and is instantly brought to rest.

(b) Find the height above the table of the line of action of this horizontal blow. [L]

12 A uniform rod, of mass M and length l, can rotate freely in a vertical plane about a smooth hinge at one end. A light inextensible string attached to the other end of the rod passes over a smooth peg which is at a height $h(> l)$ vertically above the hinge and supports a mass m hanging freely.

Show that the potential energy of the system is given by

$$\tfrac{1}{2} Mgl \cos \theta + mg\sqrt{(l^2 + h^2 - 2hl \cos \theta)} + \text{constant}$$

where θ is the inclination of the rod to the upward vertical. Prove that the positions of equilibrium in which the rod is vertical are both stable if

$$1 + \frac{l}{h} > \frac{2m}{M} > 1 - \frac{l}{h} \qquad \text{[L]}$$

13 A light rod AB, of length $2a$, can turn freely in a vertical plane about a smooth fixed hinge at A. A particle of mass m is attached at B. One end of a light elastic string, of natural length a and modulus $\dfrac{mg}{\sqrt{3}}$, is attached to B. The other end of the string is attached to a fixed point O at the same horizontal level as A. Given that $OA = 2a$ and that the angle between AB and the downward vertical at A is $\left(\dfrac{\pi}{2} - 2\theta\right)$, show that, provided the string remains taut, the potential energy of the system is

$$\frac{-2mga}{\sqrt{3}} (\sqrt{3} \sin 2\theta + 2 \cos 2\theta + 2 \sin \theta) + \text{constant.}$$

Verify that there is a position of equilibrium in which $\theta = \dfrac{\pi}{6}$ and determine whether this position is stable or unstable.　[L]

14 A uniform rod AB, of mass m and length $2a$, is free to rotate in a vertical plane about a smooth hinge at A. A light elastic string, of natural length a and modulus $\dfrac{mg}{2}$, is attached to the end B and to a small ring which can move freely on a smooth horizontal wire at a height $3a$ above A and in a vertical plane through A. Show that the system cannot be in equilibrium unless the string is vertical.

If AB makes an angle θ with the downward vertical and the string is vertical, show that the potential energy of the system is V, where

$$V = mga(\cos\theta + \cos^2\theta) + \text{constant}.$$

Determine the positions of equilibrium of the system and examine their stability.　[L]

15

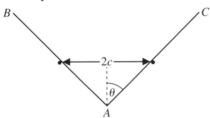

The diagram shows two uniform rods AB, AC, each of mass m and length $2a$, smoothly jointed at A and placed symmetrically, in a vertical plane, over two smooth pegs which are fixed at a distance $2c$ apart, $c < a$, on the same horizontal line. Given that each rod makes an angle θ with the upward vertical through A, show that the potential energy of the system is given by

$$2mg(a\cos\theta - c\cot\theta) + \text{constant}.$$

Hence, or otherwise, show that the equilibrium configurations occur when

$$\sin^2\theta = \frac{c}{a}.$$

Discuss the stability of the two possible positions of equilibrium.　[L]

16 A uniform rod AB, of mass m and length $2a$, can turn about a fixed smooth pivot at A. A light inextensible string is attached to the other end B of the rod, and passes through a smooth ring fixed at a point C vertically above A so that $AC = 2a$. A particle P of mass $\dfrac{m}{2}$ hangs from the other end of the string. The angle CAB is θ, where $0 \leqslant \theta \leqslant \pi$. Show that the potential energy, V, of the system is given by:

$$V = 2mga \sin\left(\frac{\theta}{2}\right) + mga \cos\theta + \text{constant}.$$

Show also that the system is in equilibrium when $\theta = \dfrac{\pi}{3}$ and when $\theta = \pi$ and investigate the stability of these positions of equilibrium. [L]

17 A small ring of mass M can move freely on a smooth circular hoop, of radius a, fixed in a vertical plane. Two light inextensible strings attached to the ring pass over two small smooth pegs situated on the hoop at the same horizontal level below the centre of the hoop. To their free ends are attached particles each of mass m. The distance between the pegs is $2a \sin \alpha$. Given that the ring is below the pegs and that $M < m \tan\left(\frac{1}{2}\alpha\right)$, prove that the number of positions of equilibrium is three or one depending whether $M > m \sin\left(\frac{1}{2}\alpha\right)$ or $M \leqslant m \sin\left(\frac{1}{2}\alpha\right)$.

Discuss the stability of the positions of equilibrium when $M > m \sin\left(\frac{1}{2}\alpha\right)$. [L]

Examination style paper

M4

Answer all questions   **Time 90 minutes**

1 To a man travelling due north at $16\,\text{km}\,\text{h}^{-1}$ the wind appeared to blow from the west. When he doubled his speed to $32\,\text{km}\,\text{h}^{-1}$ the wind appeared to blow from the north west. Find the velocity of the wind.   **(8 marks)**

2 A rigid body is acted on by three forces:
   $\mathbf{F}_1 = (4\mathbf{i} - 3\mathbf{j} + 2\mathbf{k})\,\text{N}$ at the point A with position vector $9\mathbf{i}\,\text{m}$,
   $\mathbf{F}_2 = (3\mathbf{i} + 2\mathbf{j} - 4\mathbf{k})\,\text{N}$ at the point B with position vector
   $(-\mathbf{i} - \mathbf{j} + 6\mathbf{k})\,\text{m}$, and $\mathbf{F}_3$.
   Given that the body is in equilibrium,
   (a) find $\mathbf{F}_3$
   (b) show that the vector equation of the line of action of $\mathbf{F}_3$ can be written in the form

   $$\mathbf{r} = [(5\mathbf{i} + 3\mathbf{j} - 2\mathbf{k}) + \lambda(-7\mathbf{i} + \mathbf{j} + 2\mathbf{k})]\,\text{m}$$

   where λ is a parameter.   **(10 marks)**

3 A smooth wire of length $8a$, bent into the form of an arch of a cycloid, is fixed in a vertical plane with its mid-point O at its highest point. The intrinsic equation of the curve is

   $$s = 4a\,\sin\psi\left(-\frac{\pi}{2} \leqslant \psi \leqslant \frac{\pi}{2}\right)$$

   where ψ is the angle between the tangent at O and the tangent at the point P such that the arc OP is of length s.
   A small bead of mass m is threaded on the wire.
   (a) Show that the equation of motion of the bead is

   $$\frac{\mathrm{d}^2 s}{\mathrm{d}t^2} = \frac{gs}{4a}$$

   Given that the speed of the bead at O is $\sqrt{(2ag)}$

(b) show that the speed v at P is given by

$$v^2 = 2ga(1 + 2 \sin^2 \psi)$$

(10 marks)

4 The position vector **r** metres of a particle P, relative to a fixed origin O, at time t seconds, satisfies the vector differential equation

$$\frac{d^2\mathbf{r}}{dt^2} + 2\frac{d\mathbf{r}}{dt} + 5\mathbf{r} = \mathbf{0}$$

When $t = 0$, $\mathbf{r} = \mathbf{i} + \mathbf{j}$ and $\dfrac{d\mathbf{r}}{dt} = \mathbf{i} - \mathbf{j}$.

Find **r** in terms of t and hence find the smallest possible value of t for which P is moving parallel to **j**.

(12 marks)

5 A particle P, of mass m, moves in a plane along the path with polar equation

$$r = ke^{\theta}$$

where k is a positive constant, under the action of a force of magnitude F(r) which is directed towards the pole O.

(a) Show that $F(r) = \dfrac{2mh^2}{r^3}$, where h is a constant.

(b) Explain the physical significance of the constant h.

(c) Show that the speed of P is $\dfrac{h}{r}\sqrt{2}$.

(13 marks)

6 A uniform solid cylinder, of mass M and radius r, rolls down a rough plane inclined at an angle α to the horizontal.
   (a) Find the time taken by the cylinder to move through a distance x from rest down the plane.
   (b) Find the least possible value of the coefficient of friction between the cylinder and the plane for which motion is possible.

(14 marks)

7 A particle is projected from the origin O with speed u at an angle of elevation α $\left(0 < \alpha < \dfrac{\pi}{2}\right)$ to the x-axis and it moves freely under gravity which acts along the negative y-axis. Show that the equation of the trajectory of the particle is

$$y = x \tan \alpha - \frac{gx^2}{2u^2} \sec^2 \alpha$$

A particle is projected with speed u from O on a plane inclined at $30°$ to the horizontal. The angle of projection is $60°$ to the horizontal. The particle moves in a vertical plane containing a line of greatest slope of the inclined plane. The particle first strikes the inclined plane at the point A which is higher than O.

(a) Find, in terms of u and g, the distance OA.

(b) Show that, immediately before the particle reaches A, the direction of motion of the particle makes an angle of $60°$ with the inclined plane.

(15 marks)

8 A uniform rod AB, of mass m and length $2a$, is free to rotate in a vertical plane about the point A. A light elastic string of natural length a and modulus kmg has one end attached to B and the other end attached to a fixed point O, which is vertically above A, with $AO = 2a$.

(a) Show that when AB makes an angle θ with the downward vertical the potential energy V of the system, when the string is stretched, is given by

$$V = mga \left[(4k - 1) \cos \theta - 4k \cos\left(\frac{\theta}{2}\right) \right] + \text{constant}$$

Given that $k > \frac{1}{3}$,

(b) show that the equilibrium position in which the rod is vertical with B below A is unstable.

(c) show that there is an oblique position of equilibrium which is stable.

(18 marks)

Answers

The University of London Examination and Assessment Council accepts no responsibility whatsoever for the accuracy or method of working in the answers given for examination questions.

Exercise 1A

1 (a) $(-4\mathbf{i} - 9\mathbf{j})\,\text{m}$ (b) $(3\mathbf{i} - 7\mathbf{j})\,\text{m}$

   (c) $(-5\mathbf{i} - \mathbf{k})\,\text{m}$

2 (a) $(5\mathbf{i} + 12\mathbf{j})\,\text{ms}^{-1}$ $13\,\text{ms}^{-1}$

   (b) $(4\mathbf{i} + 3\mathbf{j})\,\text{ms}^{-1}$ $5\,\text{ms}^{-1}$

   (c) $(-3\mathbf{i} - 7\mathbf{j} + 9\mathbf{k})\,\text{ms}^{-1}$ $\sqrt{139}\,\text{ms}^{-1}$

3 $(200\mathbf{i} + 470\mathbf{s})\,\text{ms}^{-1}$

4 16.00 hrs $(9\mathbf{i} + 4\mathbf{j})\,\text{km}$

5 103 km   12.20

6 (a) $60°$ to bank (upstream)

   (b) 63.5 s

7 $4.51\,\text{ms}^{-1}$ $85.4°$ to bank (downstream)

8 $052°$

9 (a) 1.45 s   (b) 3.48 m $(-2\mathbf{i} - 0.5\mathbf{j})\,\text{ms}^{-1}$

10 (a) 2s $p = 6.5$ $q = -5.5$ $(7\mathbf{i} + 8\mathbf{j} - 12\mathbf{k})\,\text{m}$

Excercise 1B

1 $\mathbf{r} = \frac{1}{4}(2\mathbf{i} - 3\mathbf{j})e^{4t} + \frac{7}{2}\mathbf{i} + \frac{3}{4}\mathbf{j}$

2 (a) $\mathbf{r} = -\frac{1}{2}\mathbf{i}\,e^{-4t} + \frac{7}{2}\mathbf{i} - 3\mathbf{j}$

   (b) 4.61 m

3 (a) $\mathbf{v} = (4\mathbf{i} + 2\mathbf{j})\,e^{2t}$ (b) $13\,300\,\text{ms}^{-1}$

4 $\mathbf{r} = e^{-t}((\mathbf{i} + \mathbf{j})\cos 2t \div (\mathbf{i} + \frac{1}{2}\mathbf{j})\sin 2t)$

   0.510 m

5 $\mathbf{r} = (2\mathbf{i} + 2\mathbf{j})\cos 4t + (\mathbf{i} - 2\mathbf{j})\sin 4t$

6 $\mathbf{r} = e^{-t}((2\mathbf{i} + \mathbf{j})t + \mathbf{i} + 2\mathbf{j})$

7 $\mathbf{r} = (3\mathbf{i} + 2\mathbf{j})\,e^{3t} - (\mathbf{i} + \mathbf{j})\,e^{-2t}$

8 $\mathbf{r} = \frac{1}{2}\,e^{2t}(\mathbf{i} + \mathbf{j} + \mathbf{k}) + \frac{3}{2}\mathbf{i} - \frac{1}{2}\mathbf{j} + \frac{7}{2}\mathbf{k}$

   $94.6\,\text{ms}^{-1}$

9 (a) $\mathbf{r} = e^{-2t}[(\cos t + 2\sin t)\mathbf{i}$
   $+ (2\cos t + 4\sin t)\mathbf{j} + (\cos t + 3\sin t)\mathbf{k}]$

   (b) 0.233 m

10 $\mathbf{r} = \frac{1}{2}\mathbf{k}e^{t} + (2\mathbf{i} + 3\mathbf{j} + \frac{1}{2}\mathbf{k})e^{-t}$

Exercise 1C

1 (a) 12 J   (b) 19 J   (c) 3 J

2 (a) 23 J   (b) 24 J   (c) 8 J

3 (a) $4.29\,\text{ms}^{-1}$ (b) $4.38\,\text{ms}^{-1}$ (c) $2.53\,\text{ms}^{-1}$

4 (a) 20 J, 10.4 J, -10 J

   (b) $\frac{308}{45}\mathbf{i} + \frac{619}{45}\mathbf{j} + \frac{70}{9}\mathbf{k}$

5 (a) $(-26\mathbf{i} - 4\mathbf{j} + 22\mathbf{k})\,\text{Nm}$

   (b) $(39\mathbf{i} + 3\mathbf{j} + 69\mathbf{k})\,\text{Nm}$

   (c) $(-13\mathbf{i} + 10\mathbf{j} - 24\mathbf{k})\,\text{Nm}$

6 (a) $(-23\mathbf{i} - 10\mathbf{j} + 25\mathbf{k})\,\text{Nm}$

   (b) $(-13\mathbf{i} + 10\mathbf{j} + 24\mathbf{k})\,\text{Nm}$

   (c) $(-19\mathbf{i} - 21\mathbf{j} - 3\mathbf{k})\,\text{Nm}$

7 (a) $(36\mathbf{i} - 72\mathbf{j} - 27\mathbf{k})\,\text{Nm}$

   (b) $(-72\mathbf{i} - 33\mathbf{j} + 54\mathbf{k})\,\text{Nm}$

8 8, 4, 1

Exercise 1D

1 (a) $(6\mathbf{i} + 4\mathbf{j} - 5\mathbf{k})\,\text{N}$

   (b) $(13\mathbf{i} + 4\mathbf{j} + 2\mathbf{k})\,\text{N}$

2 (a) $(-4\mathbf{i} - 5\mathbf{j})\,\text{N}$ (b) $(-9\mathbf{i} - 3\mathbf{j} + 3\mathbf{k})\,\text{N}$

   (c) $(-2\mathbf{i} - 3\mathbf{j} - 7\mathbf{k})\,\text{N}$

4 (a) $(2\mathbf{i} - \mathbf{j} + 8\mathbf{k})\,\text{N}$ $(8\mathbf{i} - 9\mathbf{j} - 8\mathbf{k})\,\text{Nm}$

   (b) $(2\mathbf{i} - \mathbf{j} + 8\mathbf{k})\,\text{N}$ $(14\mathbf{i} - 5\mathbf{j} - 9\mathbf{k})\,\text{Nm}$

   (c) $\mathbf{r} = \lambda(2\mathbf{i} - \mathbf{j} + 8\mathbf{k})$

      $\mathbf{r} = \mathbf{i} - \mathbf{j} + 2\mathbf{k} + \mu(2\mathbf{i} - \mathbf{j} + 8\mathbf{k})$

5 $(-10\mathbf{j} - 13\mathbf{k})\,\text{Nm}$

6 $(5\mathbf{i} + 22\mathbf{j} + 11\mathbf{k})\,\text{N}$ $(9\mathbf{i} + 20\mathbf{j} + 8\mathbf{k})\,\text{Nm}$

7 $\mathbf{R} = (9\mathbf{i} + 4\mathbf{j} + 6\mathbf{k})\,\text{N}$

   $\mathbf{r} = 7\mathbf{i} + 6\mathbf{j} + \lambda(9\mathbf{i} + 4\mathbf{j} + 6\mathbf{k})$

8 (a) $(-2\mathbf{i} - \mathbf{k})\,\text{N}$ (b) $11.4\,\text{Nm}$

Exercise 2A

1 $(\cos t + \sin t)\mathbf{i} + (\cos 2t - \sin 2t)\mathbf{j}$

2 $\mathbf{r} = vt\mathbf{i} + (ut - \tfrac{1}{2}gt^2)\mathbf{j}$

   $y = \dfrac{ux}{v} - \dfrac{gx^2}{2v^2}$

3 $\mathbf{r} = -a \sin \omega t\,\mathbf{i} - a \cos \omega t\,\mathbf{j}$

   $x^2 + y^2 = a^2$ (described in clockwise sense)

4 (a) $\dfrac{\lambda}{\theta} = \dfrac{\mu}{2r^2} + c$

   (b) $2\lambda^2 r^3 - \dfrac{\mu^2\theta^4}{r}$; $\lambda\mu r\theta^2 + \dfrac{2\mu^2\theta^3}{r}$

6 Velocity: radial $(-a\omega \sin \theta)$,

                  transverse $a\omega(1 + \cos \theta)$

   Acceleration: radial $[-a\omega^2(1 + 2\cos \theta)]$,

                      transverse $(-2a\omega^2 \sin \theta)$

7 $13a$

9 Along normal of magnitude $72\,\text{m s}^{-2}$

Exercise 3A

2 (a) $\sqrt{\left(\dfrac{a}{y}\right)}$

3 $v_0{}^2 = \dfrac{g}{8ak^2}\left[1 - (1 + 8ak)\,\text{e}^{-8ak}\right]$

6 (a) $\sqrt{(2g)}$ (b) $\dfrac{mg}{\sqrt{2}}$

Exercise 3B

7 $r = \dfrac{a}{7}$, a

Exercise 3C

5 $\arctan \tfrac{2}{3}$ and $\arctan 2$

6 $g \sec^2 \theta x^2 - 2v^2 x \tan \theta + 2v^2 h = 0$

9 (a) $551\,\text{m}$ (b) $10.6\,\text{s}$

10 (a) $30\,\text{m}$ (b) $90\,\text{m}$

Review Exercise 1

1 (c) $t = 6.7\,\text{mins}$ (d) $67.6°$

2 $\mathbf{r} = (2a - a \sin \omega t)\mathbf{i} + 2a \cos \omega t\,\mathbf{j}$
     $+ (a \sin \omega t - 3a)\mathbf{k}$

   $\mathbf{v} = -a \cos \omega t\,\mathbf{i} - 2a\omega \sin \omega t\,\mathbf{j}$
     $+ a\omega \cos \omega t\,\mathbf{k}$

   $t = (2\text{n} + 1)\dfrac{\pi}{2}$ $\min = a\sqrt{5}$ $\max = 5a$

3 $4.82\,\text{ms}^{-1}$, bearing $275°$, $240°$

4 $\mathbf{v}_B = 5\mathbf{i} + 12\mathbf{j}$, $\mathbf{v}_C = -4\mathbf{i}$

   $\mathbf{r}_B = 5t\mathbf{i} + 12t\mathbf{j}$, $\mathbf{r}_C = (80 - 4t)\mathbf{i} + 240\mathbf{j}$

   $16\,\text{s}$, $80\,\text{m}$

5 (a) $265\,\text{km h}^{-1}$ (b) $343.7°$

   (c) $43:53$

6 (a) $t = \tfrac{14}{15}\,\text{s}$ (b) $u = -2$

7 (a) $\dfrac{\omega^2}{2}\,ma^2(9 \sin^2 \omega t + 16 \cos^2 \omega t)$

   (b) $ma\omega^2(9 \cos^2 \omega t + 16 \sin^2 \omega t)^{\frac{1}{2}}$

   $\mathbf{r} = 3a \cos \omega t\,\mathbf{i} + a \sin \omega t\,\mathbf{j} - 4a \cos \omega t\,\mathbf{k}$

   $\mathbf{r} \cdot \mathbf{r} = a^2(9 \cos^2 \omega t + \sin^2 \omega t + 16 \cos^2 \omega t)$

8 $\mathbf{r} = (\text{e}^\theta - 1)\mathbf{i} + \mathbf{j}$

9 $\mathbf{r} = -\text{e}^\pi \mathbf{j}$

10 $\mathbf{r} = a(2\mathbf{i} + \mathbf{j}) - a(\mathbf{i} - \mathbf{j})\text{e}^{-\frac{3t}{T}}$

11 $\mathbf{r} = a(\mathbf{i} + \mathbf{j}) \cos nt + \dfrac{b}{n}\,(\mathbf{i} - 2\mathbf{k}) \sin nt$

12 $\mathbf{r} = (\mathbf{i} - \mathbf{k})\text{e}^{2t}$

13 $\mathbf{r} = \left(\dfrac{5a}{13} \sinh 3\omega t - \dfrac{a}{13} \sin 2\omega t\right)\mathbf{i}$
     $+ (a \cosh 3\omega t)\mathbf{j}$

14 $5\,\text{J}$

15 $7\,\text{J}$

16 240 J

17 $\dfrac{2\sqrt{53}}{27}$ $(7\mathbf{i} + 4\mathbf{j} + 4\mathbf{k})$,   52 J

18 $3\mathbf{i} + \mathbf{j} + 2\mathbf{k}$, $4\mathbf{i} - 4\mathbf{j} - 4\mathbf{k}$

19 $(4\mathbf{k} - 3\mathbf{j})$ Nm,   5 Nm

20 $2\sqrt{(a^2 + b^2 + c^2)}$

21 $(\mathbf{i} + 2\mathbf{j} + 3\mathbf{k})$ m, $a = 7, b = 2$

22 $(18\mathbf{i} - 56\mathbf{j} - 20\mathbf{k})$ Nm,   160 J,
   $(6\mathbf{i} - 5\mathbf{j} + 23\mathbf{k})$ N, $(16\mathbf{i} - 57\mathbf{j} - 17\mathbf{k})$ Nm

23 (a) 5λ (b) $-2\lambda a\mathbf{k}$ (c) $4x + 3y = 2$

24 $(-3\mathbf{i} + 4\mathbf{j} - \mathbf{k})$ N,
   $\mathbf{r} = (3\mathbf{i} - \mathbf{k}) + \lambda(3\mathbf{i} - 4\mathbf{j} + \mathbf{k})$,
   $(4\mathbf{i} + 6\mathbf{j} + 12\mathbf{k})$ Nm

25 $(3\mathbf{i} + 2\mathbf{j} - 4\mathbf{k})$ N

26 (a) $mg\cos\alpha[1 + 2\ln(2\cos\alpha)]$

31 $\dfrac{18k^4}{r^3 T^2}$, towards O

32 $r = \left(\dfrac{4a^3}{9}\right)^{\frac{1}{3}}$

33 $r = 2a + a\cos\theta$

35 (a) $\theta = 0.70$ (b) 35 m

36 (b) $R = \dfrac{5}{\cos\beta}(1 - \sin\beta)$

   (c) $H = \frac{1}{10}(25 - R^2)$

37 (a) $\dfrac{\pi}{8}$ (or 22.5° or 0.39) (b) $\dfrac{gr}{1 + r^2}$
   Consider gradient of trajectory and
   compare it with gradient of semi-circular
   cross-section of hemisphere.

38 (a) $\alpha = \arctan\left(\frac{4}{5}\right) = 38.7$ (b) $U = 20.0$
   (c) $e = 0.32$ (d) 63.5°

39 $\lambda = \dfrac{2b}{a}$, $u^2 = \dfrac{ga^2}{2b}$, $\dfrac{(a^2 + 4b^2)a}{4b^2}$

41 $\dfrac{u(u^2 + 2gh)^{\frac{1}{2}}}{g}$

42 $R_0{}^2 = \dfrac{2V^2}{g}\left(\dfrac{V^2}{2g} + H\right)$

43 $0, \arctan 5$
   (a) 240 m   (b) 2.95 s

Exercise 4A

1 mv^2

2 (a) $\frac{2}{7}\sqrt{(rg)}$ (b) $\dfrac{2}{7}\sqrt{\left(\dfrac{g}{r}\right)}$

3 (a) 3.12 rad s^{-1} (b) 12.3 N

4 $\sqrt{\left\{\dfrac{3g(2\sin\theta - 1)}{2l(1 + \cos^2\theta)}\right\}}$

5 $\dfrac{3\sqrt{3}}{13}$

6 $\dfrac{2}{3}h$

Excercise 4B

1 sliding

2 $\dfrac{w^2 d^2}{98\,\mu g}$

3 (a) 0.136   (b) 10 ms^{-1} (c) 21 J

4 (a) $\dfrac{g}{3}$ (b) $\dfrac{\sqrt{3}}{9}$ (c) $\dfrac{2g}{3}$

5 $\frac{1}{2}$

6 (a) 60.3 J   (b) 14.6 rad s^{-1}

7 $\dfrac{r\omega}{3gT}$, $\dfrac{r\omega T}{6}$

Exercise 4C

1 (a) $\dfrac{6v}{11a}$ (b) $\dfrac{2mv^2}{11}$

2 (a) $\dfrac{u}{a}$ (b) 0   (c) $\dfrac{1}{3}u$

3 (a) $\dfrac{v\sqrt{3}}{5r}$ (b) $\dfrac{v\sqrt{67}}{15}$

4 (a) $\dfrac{J\sqrt{3}}{12ml}$ (b) $\dfrac{3J^2}{16m}$

5 $\frac{4}{15}$

6 (a) $\dfrac{3u(b - x)}{4b^2 - 6bx + 3x^2}$

(b) $\dfrac{u\sqrt{3}}{2b}$,　$\left(1 - \dfrac{\sqrt{3}}{3}\right)b$

(c) $\dfrac{3mu}{2}$

7 (a) $\dfrac{8v}{9r}$　　　　　(b) $\frac{3}{8}\sqrt{(2rg)}$

Exercise 5A

1 $V = -mga\sin\theta + \dfrac{2\sqrt{3}}{3}mga\sin\left(\dfrac{\theta}{2}\right) + \text{constant}$

Stable

3 If $\theta =$ angle between rod and vertical, equilibrium positions are given by

$\theta = 0$ (unstable), $\theta = \pi$ (unstable),

$\theta = \frac{1}{3}\pi$ (stable)

4 Unstable

5 $\theta = 0$ (unstable), $\cos\theta = \frac{3}{4}$ (stable)

Exercise 5B

1 (b) $2\pi\sqrt{\left(\dfrac{ma\sqrt{2}}{\lambda}\right)}$

2 $\dfrac{\pi}{3}$,　$2\pi\sqrt{\left(\dfrac{8a}{3g}\right)}$

3 $T = 2\pi\sqrt{\left(\dfrac{3b^2 - 2a^2}{3g\sqrt{(b^2 - a^2)}}\right)}$

Review exercise 2

3 $\frac{5}{7}g\sin\alpha$,　$\frac{2}{7}\tan\alpha$

4 $\frac{7}{10}ma^2\dot{\theta}^2$,　$\frac{1}{4}\sqrt{(ag)}$,　$\sqrt{\left(\dfrac{ag}{8}\right)}$

5 (a) $\dfrac{2V^2(6\mu\cos\alpha - \sin\alpha)}{g(7\mu\cos\alpha - 2\sin\alpha)}$

(b) $\dfrac{5\mu V\cos\alpha}{a(7\mu\cos\alpha - 2\sin\alpha)}$

6 $\dfrac{2g\sin\alpha}{3}$

7 $\dfrac{4a}{3}$

8 $V\sqrt{(\cos^2\theta + \frac{1}{9}\sin^2\theta)}$ at $\arctan\left(\frac{1}{3}\tan\theta\right)$ to PO produced, $\dfrac{2V\sin\theta}{3a}$, $mv\cos\theta$ and

$\frac{1}{3}mv\sin\theta$, $\frac{1}{2}mv^2(\cos^2\theta + \frac{1}{3}\sin^2\theta)$

10 $\dfrac{9V}{10a}$, $\dfrac{19mag}{225}$, will roll

11 (b) $1.4a$

13 stable

14 $\theta = 0$　unstable

$\theta = 120°$　stable

$\theta = 180°$　unstable

15 θ acute, unstable

θ obtuse, stable

16 $\theta = \dfrac{\pi}{3}$　unstable

$\theta = \pi$　stable

17 $\theta = 0$　stable

others unstable.

Exam style paper M4

1 $16\sqrt{2}\,\text{km h}^{-1}$ from south west

2 (a) $\mathbf{F}_3 = (-7\mathbf{i} + \mathbf{j} + 2\mathbf{k})\,\text{N}$

4 $\mathbf{r} = e^{-t}[(\mathbf{i} + \mathbf{j})\cos 2t + \mathbf{i}\sin 2t]$

$t = \frac{1}{2}\arctan\frac{1}{3}$

5 (b) mh is the angular momentum of P about O

6 (a) $t = \sqrt{\left(\dfrac{3x}{g\sin\alpha}\right)}$　　(b) $\mu \geqslant \frac{1}{3}\tan\alpha$

7 $OA = \dfrac{2u^2}{3g}$

List of symbols and notation

The following symbols and notation are used in the London modular mathematics examinations:

$\{\qquad\}$	the set of
$n(A)$	the number of elements in the set A
$\{x:\quad\}$	the set of all x such that
$\in$	is an element of
$\notin$	is not an element of
$\varnothing$	the empty (null) set
$\mathscr{E}$	the universal set
$\cup$	union
$\cap$	intersection
$\subset$	is a subset of
A'	the complement of the set A
PQ	operation Q followed by operation P
$f : A \rightarrow B$	f is a function under which each element of set A has an image set in B
$f : x \mapsto y$	f is a function under which x is mapped to y
$f(x)$	the image of x under the function f
f^{-1}	the inverse relation of the function f
fg	the function f of the function g
$\circ\!\!-\!\!\circ$	open interval on the number line
$\bullet\!\!-\!\!\bullet$	closed interval on the number line
$\mathbb{N}$	the set of positive integers and zero, $\{0, 1, 2, 3, \ldots\}$
$\mathbb{Z}$	the set of integers, $\{0, \pm1, \pm2, \pm3, \ldots\}$
$\mathbb{Z}^+$	the set of positive integers, $\{1, 2, 3, \ldots\}$
$\mathbb{Q}$	the set of rational numbers
$\mathbb{Q}^+$	the set of positive rational numbers, $\{x : x \in \mathbb{Q}, x > 0\}$
$\mathbb{R}$	the set of real numbers
$\mathbb{R}_0^+$	the set of positive real numbers, $\{x : x \in \mathbb{R}, x > 0\}$
$\mathbb{C}$	the set of complex numbers
$\sqrt{}$	the positive square root
$[a, b]$	the interval $\{x : a \leqslant x \leqslant b\}$
$(a, b]$	the interval $\{x : a < x \leqslant b\}$
(a, b)	the interval $\{x : a < x < b\}$

$\lvert x \rvert$	the modulus of $x = \begin{cases} x \text{ for } x \geqslant 0 \\ -x \text{ for } x < 0 \end{cases}, x \in \mathbb{R}$
$\approx$	is approximately equal to
A^{-1}	the inverse of the non-singular matrix A
A^T	the transpose of the matrix A
det A	the determinant of the square matrix A
$\displaystyle\sum_{r=1}^{n} f(r)$	$f(1) + f(2) + \ldots + f(n)$
$\displaystyle\prod_{r=1}^{n} f(r)$	$f(1)\,f(2)\ldots f(n)$
$\dbinom{n}{r}$	the binomial coefficient $\begin{array}{l} \dfrac{n!}{r!(n-r)!} \text{ for } n \in \mathbb{Z}^+ \\[2mm] \dfrac{n(n-1)\ldots(n-r+1)}{r!} \text{ for } n \in \mathbb{Q} \end{array}$
$\exp x$	e^x
$\ln x$	the natural logarithm of x, $\log_e x$
$\lg x$	the common logarithm of x, $\log_{10} x$
arcsin	the inverse function of sin with range $[-\pi/2,\ \pi/2]$
arccos	the inverse function of cos with range $[0,\ \pi]$
arctan	the inverse function of tan with range $(-\pi/2,\ \pi/2)$
arsinh	the inverse function of sinh with range $\mathbb{R}$
arcosh	the inverse function of cosh with range $\mathbb{R}_0^+$
artanh	the inverse function of tanh with range $\mathbb{R}$
$f'(x),\ f''(x),\ f'''(x)$	the first, second and third derivatives of $f(x)$ with respect to x
$f^{(r)}(x)$	the rth derivative of $f(x)$ with respect to x
$\dot{x}, \ddot{x}, \ldots$	the first, second, ... derivatives of x with respect to t
z	a complex number, $z = x + iy = r(\cos\theta + i\sin\theta) = re^{i\theta}$
Re z	the real part of z, Re $z = x = r\cos\theta$
Im z	the imaginary part of z, Im $z = y = r\sin\theta$
z^*	the conjugate of z, $z^* = x - iy = r(\cos\theta + i\sin\theta) = re^{-i\theta}$
$\lvert z \rvert$	the modulus of z, $\lvert z \rvert = \sqrt{(x^2 + y^2)} = r$
arg z	the principal value of the argument of z, $\arg z = \theta$, where $\left.\begin{array}{l}\sin\theta = y/r \\ \cos\theta = x/r\end{array}\right\} -\pi < \theta \leqslant \pi$
$\mathbf{a}$	the vector $\mathbf{a}$
$\overrightarrow{AB}$	the vector represented in magnitude and direction by the directed line segment AB
$\hat{\mathbf{a}}$	a unit vector in the direction of $\mathbf{a}$
$\mathbf{i, j, k}$	unit vectors in the directions of the cartesian coordinate axes
$\lvert \mathbf{a} \rvert$	the magnitude of $\mathbf{a}$
$\lvert \overrightarrow{AB} \rvert$	the magnitude of $\overrightarrow{AB}$
$\mathbf{a.b}$	the scalar product of $\mathbf{a}$ and $\mathbf{b}$
$\mathbf{a} \times \mathbf{b}$	the vector product $\mathbf{a}$ and $\mathbf{b}$

A'	the complement of the event A
$P(A)$	probability of the event A
$P(A\|B)$	probability of the event A conditional on the event B
$E(X)$	the mean (expectation, expected value) of the random variable X
X, Y, R, etc.	random variables
x, y, r, etc.	values of the random variables X, Y, R, etc.
$x_1, x_2 \ldots$	observations
$f_1, f_2, \ldots$	frequencies with which the observations $x_1, x_2 \ldots$ occur
$p(x)$	probability function $P(X = x)$ of the discrete random variable X
$p_1, p_2, \ldots$	probabilities of the values $x_1, x_2 \ldots$ of the discrete random variable X
$f(x), g(x), \ldots$	the value of the probability density function of a continuous random variable X
$F(x), G(x), \ldots$	the value of the (cumulative) distribution function $P(X \leqslant x)$ of a continuous random variable X
$\text{Var}(X)$	variance of the random variable X
$B(n, p)$	binomial distribution with parameters n and p
$N(\mu, \sigma^2)$	normal distribution with mean μ and variance σ^2
μ	population mean
σ^2	population variance
σ	population standard deviation
$\bar{x}$	sample mean
s^2	unbiased estimate of population variance from a sample,

$$s^2 = \frac{1}{n-1} \sum (x - \bar{x})^2$$

ϕ	probability density function of the standardised normal variable with distribution $N(0, 1)$
Φ	corresponding cumulative distribution formation
α, β	regression coefficients
ρ	product-moment correlation coefficient for a population
r	product-moment correlation coefficient for a sample
$\sim p$	not p
$p \Rightarrow q$	p implies q (if p then q)
$p \Leftrightarrow q$	p implies and is implied by q (p is equivalent to q)

Index